The geology of the western English
Channel and its western approaches

BRITISH GEOLOGICAL SURVEY

United Kingdom Offshore Regional Report

The geology of the western English Channel and its western approaches

C D R Evans

with contributions by
R R Hillis, R W Gatliff, G A Day and J W F Edwards

LONDON HMSO 1990

Production of this report was funded by the Department of Energy and the Natural Environment Research Council

The coastline used on many maps and diagrams in this book is based on Ordnance Survey mapping

Bibliographic reference

Evans, C D R. 1990. *United Kingdom offshore regional report: the geology of the western English Channel and its western approaches.* (London: HMSO for the British Geological Survey.)

Dd 291127   C20   12/90

ISBN 11 884475 X

Contents

FIGURES

Foreword

This report describes the geology of the western English Channel and its Western Approaches, an area which includes the northern basins of the Western Approaches Trough, part of the South Celtic Sea Basin, and the Western Approaches margin. The report is one of a series that complements the published British Geological Survey (BGS) 1:250 000 geological and geophysical maps of the UK Continental Shelf. These have been compiled from data collected by the Survey and others since the 1960s. The BGS surveys and the preparation of both the maps and this series of reports have been funded largely by the Department of Energy over the past seventeen years.

During the two decades after the last war the western English Channel and its Western Approaches became the site of pioneering work in marine geology. Over the last fifteen years, the structures and sequences recognised in these early, largely geophysical, investigations have generated commercial interest. This search for hydrocarbons in the deep sedimentary basins of the area has produced new information, much of which is included here with both the BGS results and data from a wide variety of published papers. Another important source of data has been the Deep Sea Drilling Project, now the Ocean Drilling Programme, which drilled several holes on the adjacent continental slope

The report incorporates much published and unpublished data, the latter collected and provided by many unnamed individuals. Figure 14, figures 15 and 30, and figures 27, 28 and 30 are published with the permission of Seiscom Delta Ltd, Western Geophysical Ltd and GECO Exploration Services respectively. The tectonic synthesis of the area owes much to the work of R R Hillis, the sections on the basement and Variscan orogeny benefited from the ideas of G A Day and J W F Edwards, while R W Gatliff provided much in the Permo-Triassic and Jurassic chapters. The report was written and compiled by C D R Evans. In addition to those named, the report draws on the pool of BGS expertise, not only within the Marine Directorate, but also from the Land Survey and specialist groups such as Stratigraphy and Sedimentology, and Biostratigraphy. Production of the Offshore Regional Reports is coordinated by the Marine Geology Research Programme, and the series is edited by D Evans.

Peter J Cook, DSc
Director

British Geological Survey
Keyworth
Nottingham NG12 5GG

26 October 1990

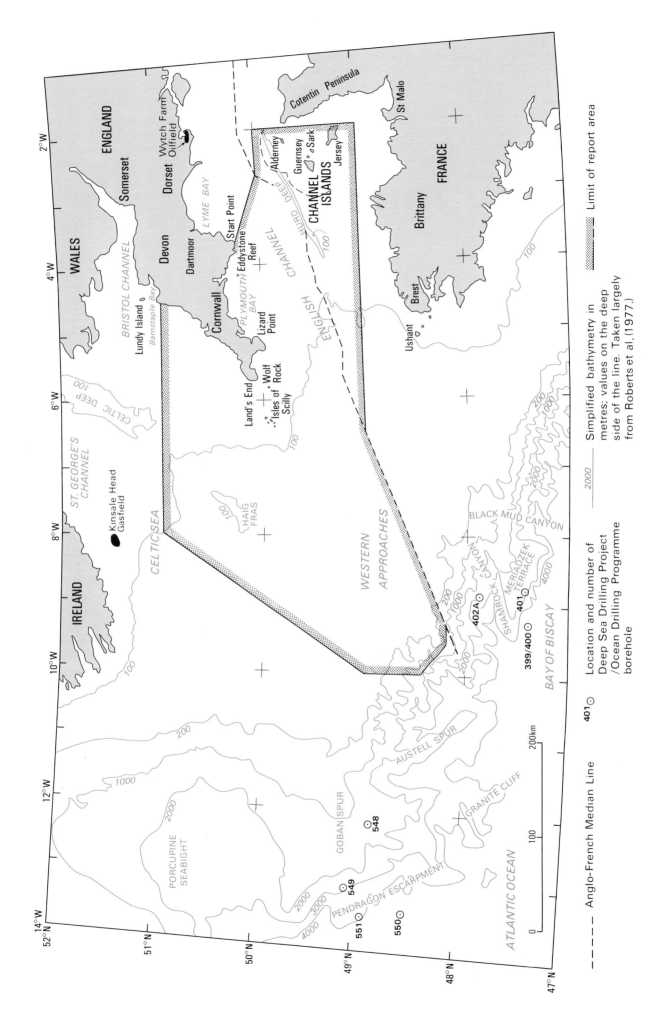

Figure 1 Location of the report area.

1 Introduction

This report describes the geology of the western English Channel and its Western Approaches, an area that measures some 500 by 200 km. The area extends eastwards to a line from Start Point to the Cotentin Peninsula in the western English Channel, northwards to 51° N, and south-westwards to the upper continental slope (Figure 1). The southern and north-western limits equate approximately to the extent of United Kingdom Designated Waters, except in the region north of Brittany.

The area forms part of the wide continental shelf to the west and south of England (Figure 2). This shelf slopes very gently south-westwards to a depth of 180 to 205 m at the shelfbreak where it passes down to the much steeper, deeply canyoned continental slope. A series of major tidal sand ridges on the outer shelf extend to the shelf edge but terminate north-eastwards on the middle shelf along a line parallel to the shelfbreak. On the inner shelf, the sea bed is generally smooth except where more resistant rocks rise above the surrounding, softer strata. Low, discontinuous, submerged coast lines are found near the coast where the shelf rises steeply to meet the shoreline.

The rocks at sea bed around the coast are resistant, metamorphosed, Palaeozoic sediments locally intruded by mainly granitic igneous bodies. Farther out on the shelf, these rocks are overlain by a sequence of Mesozoic and Tertiary strata up to 9 km thick which are disposed in a series of sedimentary basins (Figures 3 and 4). Some tens of kilometres oceanward of the shelfbreak, rocks older than the Late Cretaceous are broken into a series of irregular and rotated blocks as a consequence of extension of the upper crust during the opening of the North Atlantic. Late Cretaceous and younger strata are draped unconformably onto this complex relief, but the limited supply of sediment that has discharged onto the slope since the rifting episode has not been sufficient to completely cover the rough topography. This irregular topography is accentuated by the erosional effects of turbidity currents during periods of low sea level, and the two processes account for the complex physiography of the present slope.

The area lay on the southern fringe of the Quaternary ice sheets. At least one ice sheet reached the Isles of Scilly and may have extended eastwards into the English Channel. Isolated patches of till were dumped across the area by icebergs that floated from the main late Devensian ice mass in the north Celtic Sea.

GEOGRAPHICAL AND GEOLOGICAL TERMS

There has been confusion in published maps and papers over both geographical and geological names in the area (see Hamilton, 1979). In this report, the area is divided following Admiralty terminology into the Western Approaches and Western English Channel. This is in accord with accepted oil industry usage which restricts the Celtic Sea to the area north of about 50°30′N.

Furthermore, the names of the sedimentary basins within the area have not been used consistently. In this report, the broad major Mesozoic sedimentary basin in the region is termed the Western Approaches Trough. It is divided into a northern sector, mostly in UK waters, con-

taining the Melville, St Mary's and Plymouth Bay basins; and a southern sector containing the Brittany and Southwest Channel basins (Figure 4). The northern flank of the Western Approaches Trough is the Cornubian Platform, an offshore extension of the Cornubian Massif; the platform and massif together constitute the Cornubian Ridge. At the northern limit of the report area, the South Celtic Sea Basin abuts against the flanks of the Cornubian Platform. Figure 5 shows a stratigraphic column incorporating the terms used in the report along with an indication of the age range of each unit taken from Snelling (1985).

PREVIOUS RESEARCH

The English Channel and its Western Approaches have been the site of many pioneering investigations in marine geology. An early review of dredge results by the Marine Biological Association at Plymouth (Crawshay, 1908; Worth, 1908) recognised that the onshore crystalline rocks extend a short distance into the English Channel, and that Mesozoic and Tertiary rocks crop out at sea bed farther out.

Dangeard (1923; 1929), reviewing sea-bed samples from the area, reported Nummulites south of the Isles of Scilly, and Eocene molluscs around Guernsey. Large angular clasts recovered from the Channel, especially from the Hurd Deep (Fosse Centrale), were considered to have been transported by floating ice.

In 1938 and 1939, Bullard and Gaskell (1941) carried out the first seismic refraction experiments from Plymouth Bay to the edge of the shelf. They established that the outer shelf was underlain by over 2400 m of strata with a velocity of up to 2900 m/s, which they considered to be of post-Palaeozoic age. Parallel investigations into the gravity anomalies of the area using a submarine were curtailed by the approach of war, but in 1946 a west-south-westerly line run across the report area identified negative gravity anomalies in the English Channel (Browne and Cooper, 1950).

Between 1947 and 1949, Hill and King (1953) shot a series of east–west refraction lines and constructed a geological cross-section along a traverse running for some 80 km south of Plymouth. They correlated their refraction results with 66 samples of bedrock collected using a gravity corer. The western English Channel was described as a trough filled with New Red Sandstone (Permo-Triassic) and thin Lower Jurassic strata, unconformably overlain by Upper Cretaceous Chalk with thin patches of Tertiary rocks lying in synclinal basins.

In 1952, refraction experiments were conducted westwards from the English Channel into the Atlantic by Hill and Laughton (1954). Their cross-sections of the continental shelf gave the first indication of the relationship between the sequences on the inner shelf and those of the deep ocean. These, and new refraction and gravity experiments, resulted in maps of the Western Approaches showing the depth to the metamorphic basement and Palaeozoic floor, and the thickness of Permian and younger sediments (Day et al., 1956). Commercial and British Institutions Reflection Profiling Syndicate (BIRPS) continuous

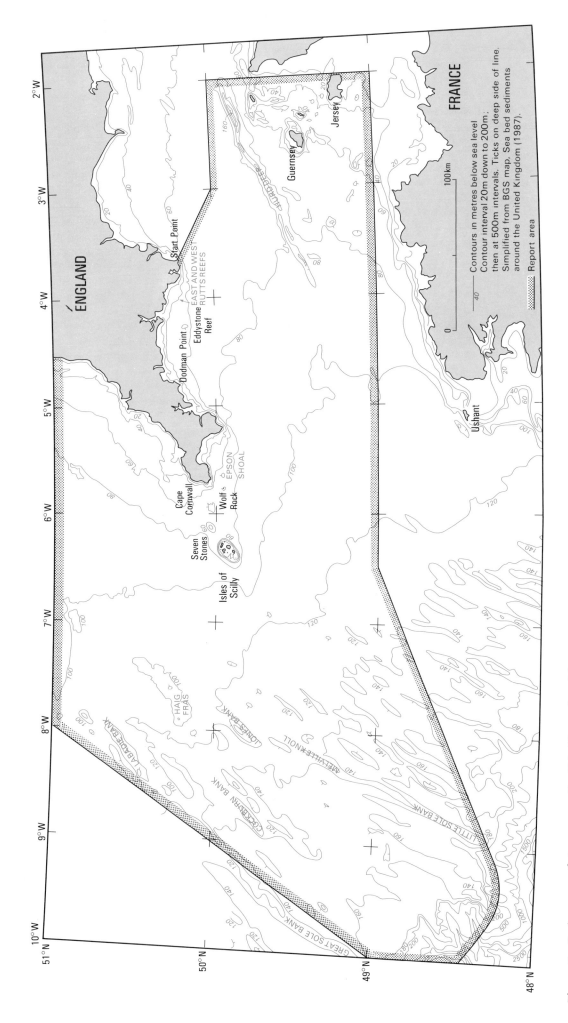

Figure 2 Bathymetry of the western English Channel and its western approaches.

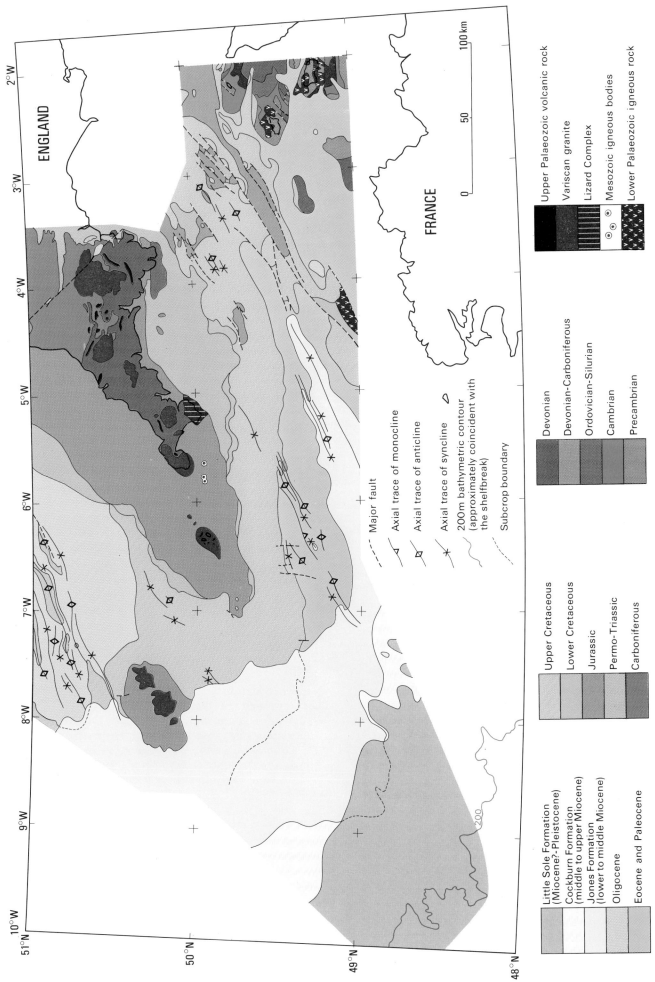

Figure 3 Surface geology of the report area (strata at sea bed or beneath the late Pleistocene and Holocene deposits).

3

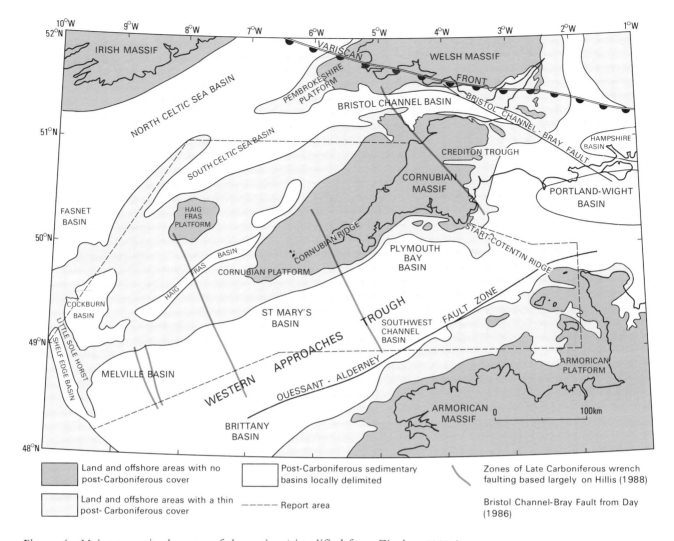

Figure 4 Major tectonic elements of the region (simplified from Ziegler, 1987a).

reflection profiles shot subsequently have demonstrated that the Palaeozoic floor lies at a considerably greater depth than shown on these maps, and that the high velocities observed at shallow depth relate to units within the Permo-Triassic sequence (Day, 1986; BIRPS and ECORS, 1986).

The first magnetic surveys in Plymouth Bay (Allan, 1961) showed a large anomaly some 27 km south of the Eddystone Reef which was interpreted as a basic mass, resembling the Lizard Complex, raised on a thrust plane. Magnetic surveys farther west (Hill and Vine, 1965) showed a series of linear anomalies over the Western Approaches Trough, which were correlated with the structural trends in the Hercynian basement described by Day et al. (1956).

The first results of continuous reflection profiling provided a better understanding of the geometry and stratigraphic relationships of units exposed at the sea bed. Curry et al. (1965a), using sparker and boomer profiles together with gravity cores, were able to delimit and subdivide the Upper Cretaceous in the deepest part of the western English Channel. Hersey and Whittard (1966) ran seismic profiles along the outer shelf and upper slope which showed the gently warped, prograding nature of the near surface units, and their abrupt truncation on the upper slope. Geologists based at Bristol University concentrated on mapping the area by detailed analysis of gravity core samples and seismic profiles (Curry et al., 1962; Curry et al., 1965b; Curry et al., 1972; Smith et al., 1965). Similar

work in the French sector, mostly by the Bureau de Recherches Géologiques et Miniéres (BRGM), was synthesised in the 'Colloque sur la géologie de la Manche' held at Paris in 1971 (Pomerol, 1972; Andreieff et al., 1975).

The major topographic features of the slope and its highly incised nature were described by Day (1959) and Francis (1962). Cartwright and Stride (1958) recognised large sandwaves near the shelf edge while Hadley (1964) identified the direction of movement of these bedforms and correlated the occurrence of canyons with an adequate supply of sand cascading off the shelf. However, the full topographic complexity of the slope was not revealed until the publication of the results of a GLORIA long-range sidescan sonar survey (Kenyon et al., 1978) and a limited swathe bathymetry (Sea Beam) survey (Pastouret et al., 1982).

ACTIVITY OF THE BRITISH GEOLOGICAL SURVEY (BGS)

In 1966 the British Geological Survey (then called the Institute of Geological Sciences) started a reconnaissance survey of the UK Continental Shelf. The results were compiled in a series of 1:250 000-scale maps displaying solid geology, Quaternary geology, sea-bed sediments, gravity anomalies and aeromagnetic anomalies. No separate Quaternary geology sheets have been produced for the report area because of the thin and discontinuous nature of

4

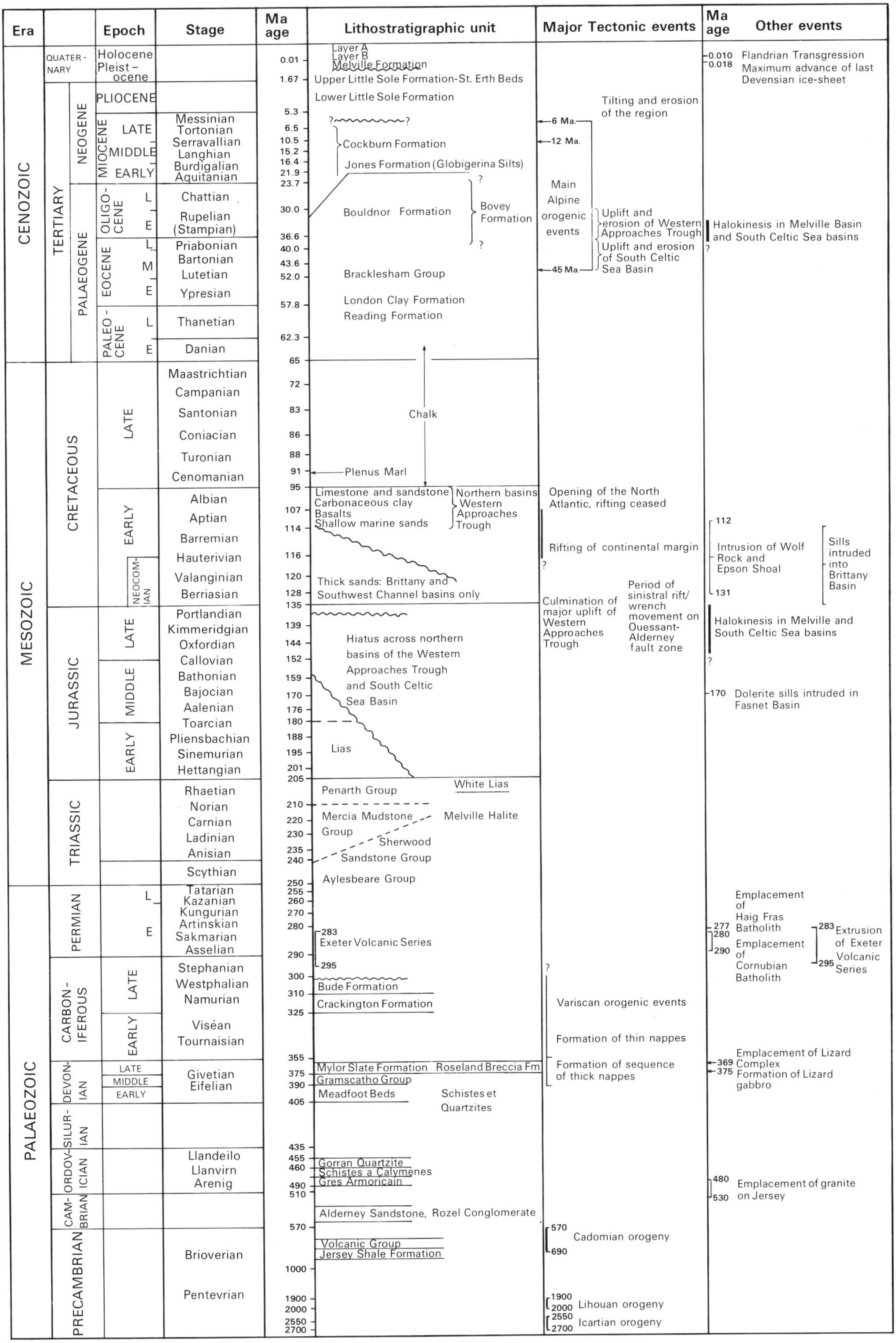

Figure 5 Table of stratigraphic units. Ages and terminology largely after Snelling (1985).

Era		Epoch	Stage	Ma age	Lithostratigraphic unit	Major Tectonic events	Ma age	Other events
CENOZOIC	QUATERNARY	Holocene Pleistocene		0.01 / 1.67	Layer A / Layer B / Melville Formation / Upper Little Sole Formation–St. Erth Beds / Lower Little Sole Formation		0.010 / 0.018	Flandrian Transgression / Maximum advance of last Devensian ice-sheet
	TERTIARY	NEOGENE — MIOCENE — LATE / MIDDLE / EARLY	PLIOCENE / Messinian / Tortonian / Serravallian / Langhian / Burdigalian / Aquitanian	5.3 / 6.5 / 10.5 / 15.2 / 16.4 / 21.9 / 23.7	Cockburn Formation / Jones Formation (Globigerina Silts)	Tilting and erosion of the region / ←6 Ma. / ←12 Ma. / Main Alpine orogenic events		
		PALAEOGENE — OLIGOCENE L/E	Chattian / Rupelian (Stampian)	30.0 / 36.6	Bouldnor Formation · Bovey Formation	Uplift and erosion of Western Approaches Trough		Halokinesis in Melville Basin and South Celtic Sea basins
		EOCENE L/M/E	Priabonian / Bartonian / Lutetian / Ypresian	40.0 / 43.6 / 52.0 / 57.8	Bracklesham Group / London Clay Formation	Uplift and erosion of South Celtic Sea Basin / ←45 Ma.		
		PALAEOCENE L/E	Thanetian / Danian	62.3	Reading Formation			
MESOZOIC	CRETACEOUS	LATE	Maastrichtian / Campanian / Santonian / Coniacian / Turonian / Cenomanian	65 / 72 / 83 / 86 / 88 / 91 / 95	Chalk / Plenus Marl			
		EARLY	Albian / Aptian / Barremian / Hauterivian / Valanginian (NEOCOMIAN) / Berriasian	107 / 114 / 116 / 120 / 128 / 135	Limestone and sandstone / Carbonaceous clay / Basalts / Shallow marine sands · Northern basins / Western Approaches Trough / Thick sands: Brittany and Southwest Channel basins only	Opening of the North Atlantic, rifting ceased / Rifting of continental margin / Culmination of major uplift of Western Approaches Trough	112 / 131	Intrusion of Wolf Rock and Epson Shoal · Sills intruded into Brittany Basin
	JURASSIC	LATE	Portlandian / Kimmeridgian / Oxfordian	139 / 144 / 152	Hiatus across northern basins of the Western Approaches Trough and South Celtic Sea Basin	Period of sinistral rift/wrench movement on Ouessant-Alderney fault zone		Halokinesis in Melville and South Celtic Sea basins
		MIDDLE	Callovian / Bathonian / Bajocian / Aalenian	159 / 170 / 176			170	Dolerite sills intruded in Fasnet Basin
		EARLY	Toarcian / Pliensbachian / Sinemurian / Hettangian	180 / 188 / 195 / 201 / 205	Lias			
	TRIASSIC		Rhaetian / Norian / Carnian / Ladinian / Anisian / Scythian	210 / 220 / 230 / 235 / 240 / 250	Penarth Group · White Lias / Mercia Mudstone Group · Melville Halite / Sherwood Sandstone Group / Aylesbeare Group			
PALAEOZOIC	PERMIAN	L / E	Tatarian / Kazanian / Kungurian / Artinskian / Sakmarian / Asselian	255 / 260 / 270 / 280 / 290 / 295	Exeter Volcanic Series		277 / 280 / 290 / 283 / 295	Emplacement of Haig Fras Batholith / Emplacement of Cornubian Batholith · Extrusion of Exeter Volcanic Series
	CARBONIFEROUS	LATE	Stephanian / Westphalian / Namurian	300 / 310 / 325	Bude Formation / Crackington Formation	Variscan orogenic events		
		EARLY	Viséan / Tournaisian	355		Formation of thin nappes		
	DEVONIAN	LATE / MIDDLE / EARLY	Givetian / Eifelian	375 / 390 / 405	Mylor Slate Formation · Roseland Breccia Fm / Gramscatho Group / Meadfoot Beds · Schistes et Quartzites	Formation of sequence of thick nappes	369 / 375	Emplacement of Lizard Complex / Formation of Lizard gabbro
	ORDOVICIAN–SILURIAN		Llandeilo / Llanvirn / Arenig	435 / 455 / 460 / 490 / 510	Gorran Quartzite / Schistes à Calymènes / Grès Armoricain		480 / 530	Emplacement of granite on Jersey
	PRECAMBRIAN — CAMBRIAN		Brioverian	570 / 1000	Alderney Sandstone, Rozel Conglomerate / Volcanic Group / Jersey Shale Formation	Cadomian orogeny	570 / 690	
			Pentevrian	1900 / 2000 / 2550 / 2700		Lihouan orogeny / Icartian orogeny	1900 / 2000 / 2550 / 2700	

5

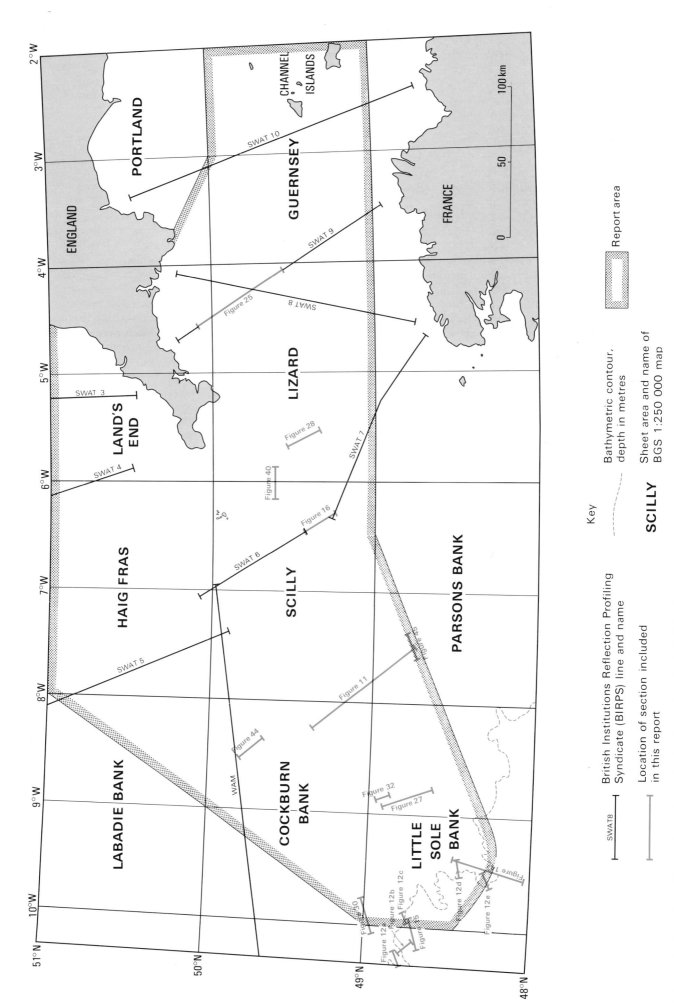

Figure 6 Location of BIRPS profiles and seismic sections included in the report.

Key

SWAT8 ⊢——⊣ British Institutions Reflection Profiling Syndicate (BIRPS) line and name

⊢——⊣ Location of section included in this report

— — — Bathymetric contour, depth in metres

SCILLY Sheet area and name of BGS 1:250 000 map

▓▓ Report area

Quaternary sediments on this portion of the shelf. The limits and names of the BGS maps in the report area are shown in Figure 6 and inside the back cover.

The BGS occupied 2855 sites in the area; a vibrocorer and grab were used at 391 of these sites and a gravity corer and grab at 2087. The *Whitethorn* drilling operation which BGS ran between 1970 to 1975 drilled only one borehole in the report area, number 74/41 on the Eddystone Reef (Figure 7). In 1975, the *Wimpey Sealab* was used to drill one borehole (SLS Trial) in the Scilly sheet (Jenkins, 1977), and returned the following year to drill an additional 28 holes across the report area (Figure 7). Although recovery was poor through the Chalk, the results provided valuable information on the stratigraphy of the Lower Cretaceous sediments (Lott et al., 1980). The shallow boreholes drilled in 1979 and 1981 employing the vessels *Surveyor* and *Mariner* cored the Miocene succession on the middle shelf (Evans and Hughes, 1984). The results of all BGS boreholes drilled in the region are given in Parkin and Crosby (1982), and their locations are shown on Figure 7; associated biostratigraphic work is summarised in Warrington and Owens (1977) and Wilkinson and Halliwell (1980).

In 1977, the Department of Energy funded four wells in the area in order to assist with interpretation of seismic profiles and to encourage exploration for hydrocarbons. These are termed the Zephyr wells after the semisubmersible rig used (Evans et al., 1981).

HYDROCARBON EXPLORATION

Hydrocarbon exploration away from coastal locations began with the shooting of speculative multichannel seismic profiles in parts of the area in the early 1970s. In the 1972 UK Fourth Round of licence allocation, blocks were awarded in the South Celtic Sea Basin, and the first well (93/2-1) was drilled by BP in 1974 (Figure 7). Subsequent licence awards led to continued seismic exploration and the drilling of the first well on the outer shelf (72/10-1A) by Britoil in 1979. A total of 19 exploration wells have been drilled to date in the UK sector, though no commercial shows of hydrocarbons have been reported. Most of the allocated blocks across the UK sector of the shelf in the report area have been relinquished following these poor initial results. Simplified logs of many of the

wells are presented in Figure 8. All well depths in this report are referred to sea level and simplified to the nearest metre. The data from many of the wells have now been released on microfiche by the Department of Energy (Fannin, 1989).

DEEP SEA DRILLING PROJECT

In 1976, on Leg 48 of the Deep Sea Drilling Project (DSDP), the *Glomar Challenger* drilled three sites (numbers 399/400, 401 and 402A) on the continental slope south-west of the report area (Figure 1). In this report, the zone in which these sites were drilled is referred to as the Western Approaches margin, to separate it from the Bay of Biscay margin to the south, and the Goban Spur margin to the north and west (see Figure 13). The wells were drilled in water depths between 2339 m and 4399 m, and proved a sequence of Mesozoic to Recent sediments which allowed a definitive correlation with reflectors seen on seismic profiles from the area (Montadert et al., 1979).

In 1980, Leg 80 of DSDP (renamed the International Phase of Ocean Drilling—IPOD) drilled four sites (numbers 548, 549, 550 and 551) on the Goban Spur margin (Figure 1). The results refined ideas on the Tertiary and Quaternary palaeoceanographic influences on sedimentation, and proved a more complete sequence of these units than had been recovered during Leg 48 (de Graciansky and Poag, 1985).

BRITISH INSTITUTIONS REFLECTION PROFILING SYNDICATE (BIRPS)

In 1984, BIRPS ran several deep multichannel seismic profiles (Figure 6), termed South West Approaches Traverses (SWAT), in order to establish the deep crustal structure of the region (BIRPS and ECORS, 1986). An additional line (Western Approaches Margin—WAM) was run in 1985 from the west of the Isles of Scilly to beyond the oceanic–continental crust boundary (McGeary et al., 1987). Data were recorded to 15 seconds two-way travel time (TWTT) along these lines and reflectors were imaged from below the Mohorovičić Discontinuity (Moho), which is at a depth of about 30 km across the region.

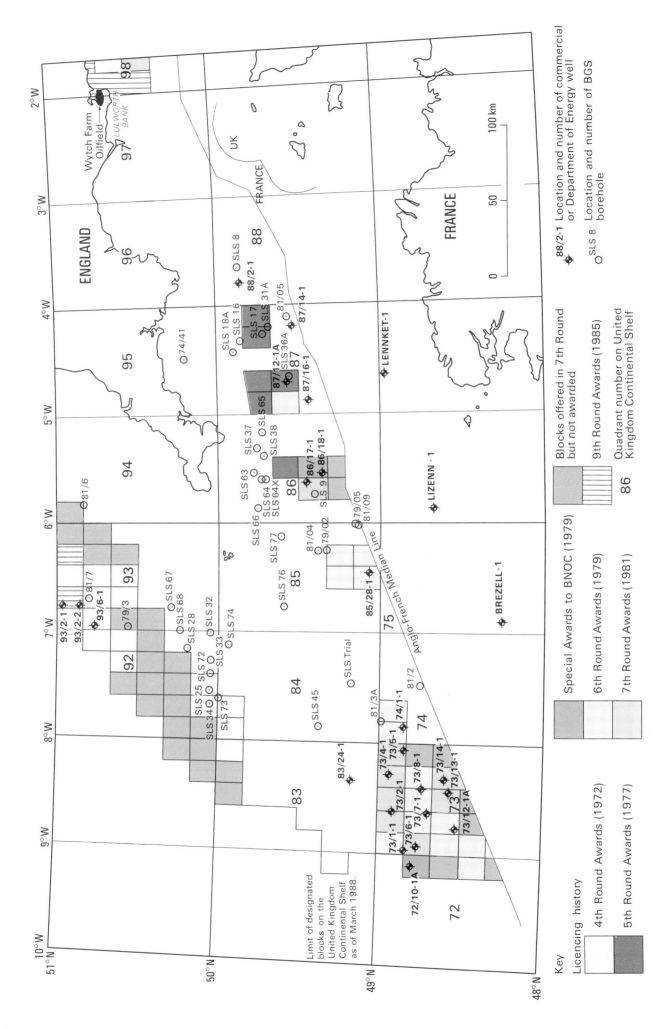

Figure 7 Details of hydrocarbon licences, and location of boreholes and wells.

8

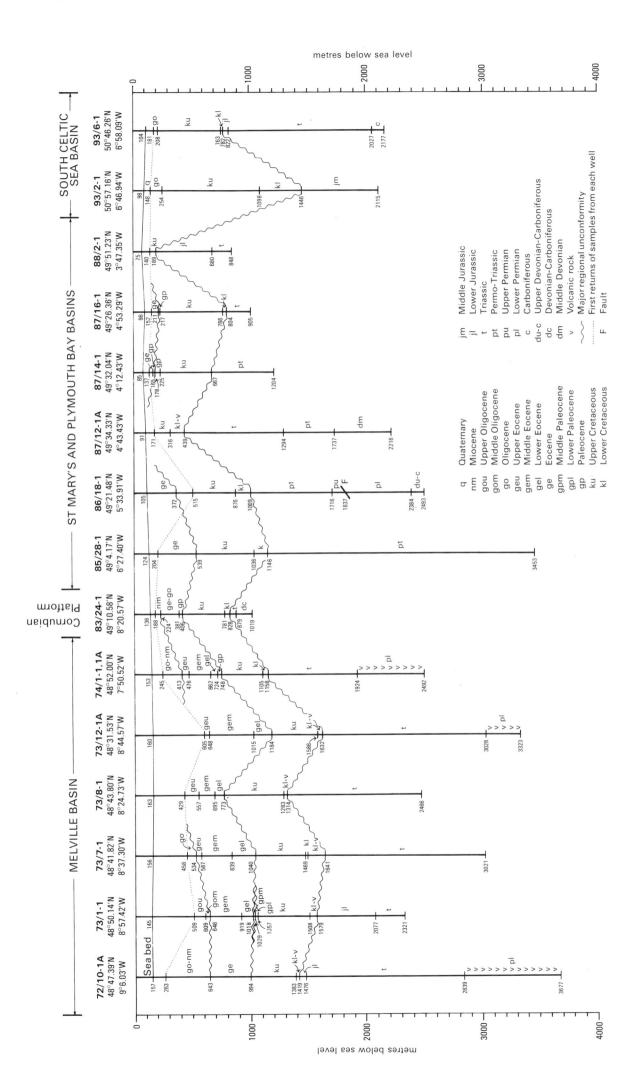

Figure 8 Simplified stratigraphic logs of selected wells from the report area.

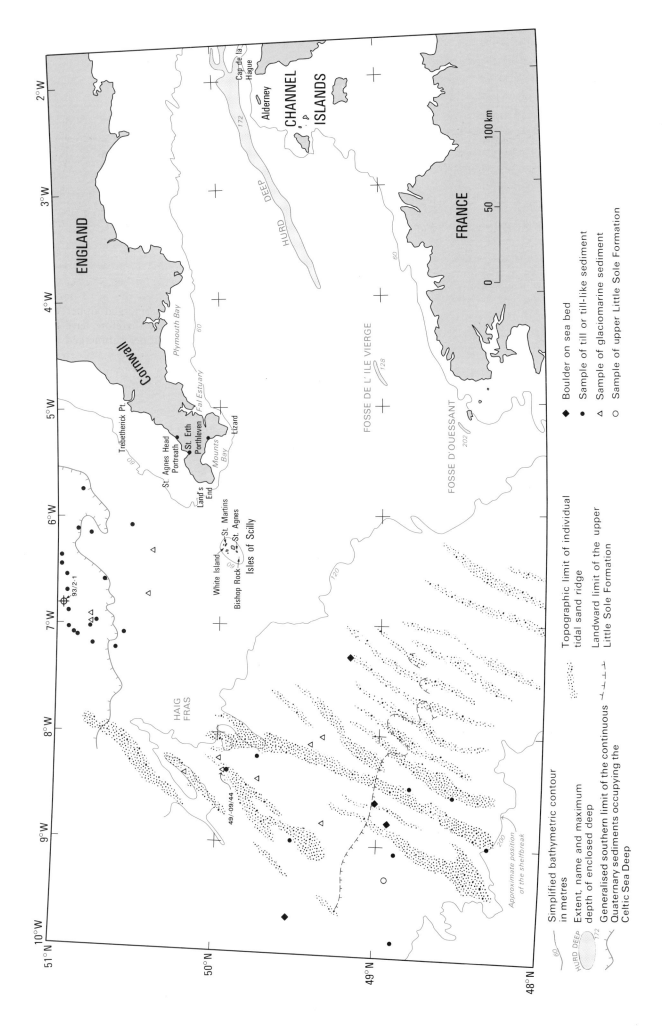

Figure 9 Location of Quaternary features.

Legend:

- Boulder on sea bed (♦)
- Sample of till or till-like sediment (●)
- Sample of glaciomarine sediment (△)
- Sample of upper Little Sole Formation (○)

60 — Simplified bathymetric contour in metres

HURD DEEP 172 — Extent, name and maximum depth of enclosed deep

Generalised southern limit of the continuous Quaternary sediments occupying the Celtic Sea Deep

Topographic limit of individual tidal sand ridge

Landward limit of the upper Little Sole Formation

Approximate position of the shelfbreak

Map labels:
ENGLAND, Cornwall, Plymouth Bay, Trebetherick Pt., St. Agnes Head, Portreath, St. Erth, Porthleven, Land's End, Mounts Bay, Lizard, Fal Estuary, White Island, St. Martins, St. Agnes, Bishop Rock, Isles of Scilly, HAIG FRAS, 93/2-1, 49/-09/44, CHANNEL ISLANDS, Cap de la Hague, Alderney, HURD DEEP, FRANCE, FOSSE DE L'ILE VIERGE, FOSSE D'OUESSANT

10

2 Physiography

The offshore area may be divided into five bathymetric zones (Figure 9):

1. A narrow, steep coastal zone extending down to 50 or 70 m.
2. A wide, almost featureless inner shelf extending down to about 120 m.
3. The usually rugged, rocky shoals which rise above the general level of the inner shelf.
4. A more irregular outer shelf, extending from 120 m down to the shelfbreak at 180 to 205 m.
5. A steep continental slope extending from the shelfbreak down to about 4500 m.

THE COASTAL ZONE

The coast surrounding Devon and Cornwall is mostly backed by cliffs which rise steeply to heights in excess of 100 m (Stephens, 1970). These cliffs are best developed along the northern coast of the peninsula, whereas along the southern coast they are broken by rias where the sea penetrates along mature valleys, such as at the Fal Estuary. Offshore, away from these valleys, the sea bed slopes steeply from the foreshore to a depth of about 50 to 70 m where it passes into the much flatter inner shelf. The near-shore zone is steepest around the major promontaries of Land's End and the Lizard, and gentler away from the north Cornwall coast.

Adjacent to the cliffed coastline, the coastal zone from the foreshore to a depth of about 7 to 20 m is a continuation of the modern cliff slope (Donovan and Stride, 1975), though slopes are gentler in bays lacking a cliffed sur-round. The sea bed below this depth, down to about 50 to 70 m, continues as a series of cliffs (marking submerged coast lines) separated by near horizontal benches (Figure 10). There may be a cover of sediments across the benches, but its thickness is limited and the bedrock features are not generally masked. Not all of these cliffs coincide with major lithological boundaries. Three degraded, discontinuous coast lines occur offshore at depths of 38 to 49 m, 49 to 58 m and 58 to 69 m below OD, and appear to deepen to the west (Donovan and Stride, 1975). The offshore longitudinal profiles of rias along the south coast of Devon slope down to no lower than the 37 m isobath, which is near the base of the submerged upper cliffs (Kelland, 1975). These valleys may therefore have been formed at the same time as the upper submerged coast lines. To the west, in Falmouth Bay, these valleys are now infilled and have little topographic expression, but their infill of sand, clay and gravel extends down to a depth of 56 m below OD. A peat at 32 m below OD recovered from a buried channel in Mounts Bay yielded a radiocarbon age of 12 070 years BP (Taylor and Goode, 1987).

Pantin and Evans (1984) considered the initial planation of the inner shelf to have been related to the Oligocene uplift and erosion of the region. The major planation surface across southern Cornwall, termed the Reskajeage Surface, was also formed during the mid-Tertiary (Walsh et al., 1987). Donovan and Stride (1975) and Wood (1976) suggest a Miocene age for the erosion of the submerged coast lines. A late Miocene to Pliocene event truncated the early Miocene Jones Formation across the outer shelf, and this erosional surface extends almost undeformed onto the peneplaned basement rocks of the inner shelf and coastal

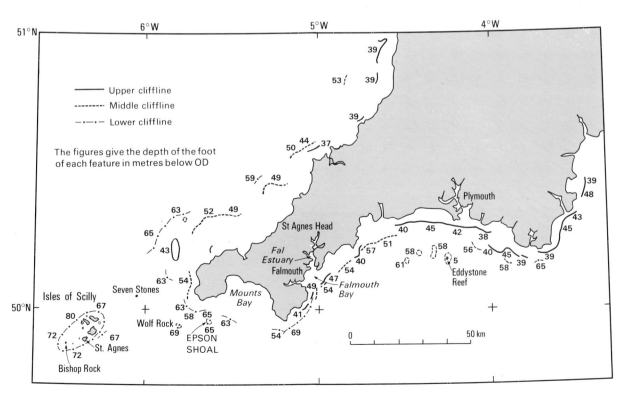

Figure 10 Submerged coast lines around south-west England. After Donovan and Stride (1975).

11

zone. The inner shelf would thus have been subjected to erosion during both the Oligocene and the late Miocene to Pliocene; the more substantial erosion took place during the earlier event, and the present submerged cliffs may be the result of modification of the older surface during the later event. The occurrence of three sets of coast lines may be due to tectonic warping of the area rather than specific still stands in sea level. The inner shelf would have been traversed by wave action on numerous occasions as sea level fluctuated through the Pleistocene, but these episodes were short-lived, and erosionally less effective than the earlier tectonically related planation events.

THE INNER SHELF

The transition from the coastal zone to the inner shelf is smooth along the north coast of the Cornish peninsula, but much more abrupt along the southern headlands and shoals. North-westwards from Cornwall and southwards from Plymouth Bay, the inner shelf has a slope of about 1:1500. The Quaternary sediment cover is thin and the form of the sea bed is a close approximation to that of the bedrock erosion surface. The sea-bed profile crosses diverse lithologies with almost no change in relief (compare Figures 2 and 3), and rugged topography is absent except where the most resistant igneous rocks crop out. Wood (1976) regarded the smooth transition of the erosion surface across widely varying rocks as the result of erosion by a gradually transgressing sea, though the platform is wider than any modern wave-cut bench (Walsh et al., 1987).

Numerous enclosed deeps are incised into the continental shelf around the British Isles (Wingfield, 1990); the only example in this area is the Hurd Deep, a 150 km-long, linear feature in the western English Channel that reaches a maximum depth of 172 m (Figure 2). Minor extensions to the deep are preserved south-westwards as far as Ushant. The feature was probably cut during the late Pleistocene, though its origins are uncertain (see p. 75).

SHOALS

Shoals of more resistant, usually igneous, rocks occur on the inner shelf. The largest of these is that which forms the Isles of Scilly, a series of low islands composed of granite, with a maximum height of 51 m above OD and bounded by a steep, narrow, offshore coastal zone. To the east of the island of St Agnes, the sea floor descends from the shore to a depth greater than 50 m in a distance of about 300 m, and a similar physiography occurs to the west of the Bishop Rock. In both cases the sea bed flattens out dramatically at a depth of about 50 m, though Donovan and Stride (1975) mark the base of the lower cliff series around the islands at between 67 and 80 m.

Haig Fras, about 150 km slightly north of west from Land's End, is a shoal centred on three granitic bodies covering an area of about 45 by 15 km. One part of the shoal rises to within 40 m of the sea surface, though the general level of the shoal is only some 20 m above the surrounding shelf which is at a depth of 100 to 110 m. A series of four benches up to nearly a kilometre across occurs on the eastern side of the shoal at water depths of between 91 and 104 m. The region of highest peaks is along the north-western part of the granite outcrop, and the steepest slope is often at the granite perimeter. The shoal is traversed by a series of long, linear, valley-like features caused by differential erosion along joint planes, and the roughest sea bed is formed of in-situ, subrounded blocks up to 2 m across separated by deeply incised joint planes infilled with sand. This sea-bed form is comparable with the granite tors in Cornwall, which suggests that the erosion was subaerial rather than submarine, though this could have occurred during a number of occasions between the Early Cretaceous and late Pleistocene.

The Wolf Rock, Epson Shoal (Harrison et al., 1977), Seven Stones and the Eddystone Reef (Phillips, 1964) are all examples of igneous bodies that have resisted the erosion which planed off the surrounding sea bed, and all presently either break the sea surface or come close to it (Figure 10).

THE OUTER SHELF

The 120 m isobath forms the boundary between the inner and outer shelf in the area, and trends across the shelf with north-west to south-east alignment parallel to the shelf-break (Figures 2 and 9). To the south-west of this line, the topography of the shelf is dominated by the large tidal sand ridges (Figures 9 and 11) whose north-eastern termination is abrupt and depth controlled. The ridges range up to 60 m in height and 200 km in length, with a spacing of 10 to 15 km; they rest on a smooth, flat, late Pleistocene erosional surface that forms the top of the upper Little Sole Formation. Some of the ridges are asymmetric in profile but there is no regularity in this asymmetry either along individual ridges or across the series. Their profile varies

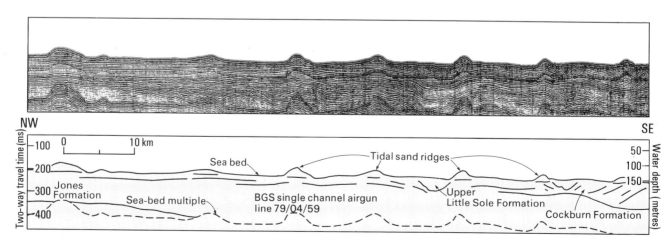

Figure 11   Seismic profile showing a series of tidal sand ridges. For location see Figure 6.

from well rounded with only one high point to highly irregular forms with several crests, and in general the greater the relief, the smoother the profile. The general trend of the ridges is 030°, but the axes show gentle curvature. On the outer shelf, the major axis of the tidal velocity ellipse runs approximately parallel to the ridges, but on the middle shelf the axis runs about 20° clockwise with respect to the ridges.

Stride et al. (1982) described the ridges as moribund, by which they meant that they were formed during a period when sea level was lower and that they are now in a state of decay. Pantin and Evans (1984) used a model of sand bank formation proposed by Huthnance (1982) to deduce that present tidal conditions cannot account for the size and spacing of the ridges. However, during the late Devensian the water depth at the shelf edge was about 60 m, and in such conditions the Huthnance model supports the formation of the ridges, although it demands a tidal ellipse running oblique to the shelf edge. Numerical modelling of the semidiurnal (M_2) tidal streams in the Celtic Sea with a sea level lowered by 100 m indicates tidal currents about twice as strong as those at present (Belderson et al., 1985); such currents would have been sufficient to generate and maintain the tidal sand ridges. The modelling also indicates that the tidal ellipse would have been rotated clockwise during this period, which is in the correct sense for ridge formation.

As the Flandrian transgression proceeded, the ridges advanced landward until they reached that part of the shelf where the supply of sediment was not adequate to feed their extension. At this juncture, approximately equivalent to the 120 m isobath, their landward growth stopped. Evidence of glacial sediments on the ridge flanks indicates that they formed before the final withdrawl of ice from the outer shelf region, and Scourse (in press) proposed that they had achieved their present form as the last ice sheet in the Celtic Sea Deep to the north floated and broke up.

THE SHELFBREAK

The shelfbreak is the boundary between the continental shelf and slope, and is placed at the maximum change in inclination of the sea bed (Vanney and Stanley, 1983). In the report area, the depth of the shelfbreak ranges from 180 to 205 m and varies in profile from being a distinct, low, degraded scarp (Figure 12c) to a smooth gradual increase in inclination (Figure 12e). These variations in profile may also be strongly incised by the heads of submarine canyons (Figure 12a). A tidal sand ridge at 48°47′N 10°16′W, at the shelf edge, shows a slump scar on its south-western flank as a result of lateral encroachment of a canyon head (Figure 12a), which dates the latest slumping on the slope as post-Devensian.

At least two minor valleys some 60 to 80 m deep and about 1 to 2 km across are incised into the outer shelf (BGS Little Sole Bank Sea Bed Sediment sheet). One has a flat floor and the other a V-shaped profile, and they link into the canyon system as modern feeders for sand moving down from the shelf onto the slope. Hadley (1964) recognised that sand moves off the outer shelf across the shelfbreak into the canyons, although tidal conditions may impose a bedload parting zone at the shelfbreak (Heathershaw and Codd, 1986).

The planar nature of continental shelves around the world is attributed to marine erosion, specifically during glacial episodes when the fall of sea level results in widespread erosion by wave action (Kennett, 1982). Yet the

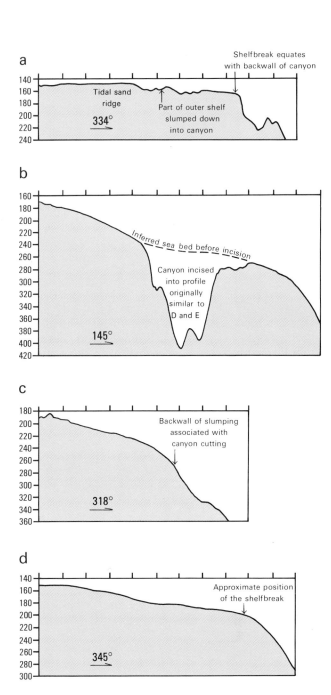

Figure 12 Profiles across the shelfbreak. For locations see Figure 6.

shelfbreak in this area is 60 to 70 m deeper than the sea level reached during the last glacial maximum (Bouysse et al., 1976), when the global fall in sea level was probably the lowest of any glacially related lowstand during the Pleistocene (Cronin, 1983). This rules out the possibility that the outer shelf was planated to these depths by a lowstand related to an earlier Pleistocene glaciation. The depth of the shelfbreak varies around north-west Europe, and is some 30 to 60 m shallower off north-west Scotland and the Gulf of Aquitaine than in the Western Approaches. Pan-

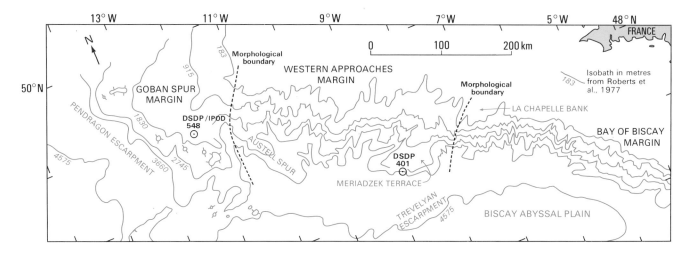

Figure 13 The bathymetry of the continental slope.

tin and Evans (1984) attributed this variation to Quaternary tectonic warping which may have been the final manifestation of late Tertiary tilting of the region, although glacio-isostatic influences also need to be considered.

THE CONTINENTAL SLOPE

The continental slope is the zone between the shallower continental shelf and the deeper abyssal plain. It is here topographically divisible into three along-slope sectors (Figure 13). The Bay of Biscay margin has an average slope of 4° and is regularly canyoned along its length, whereas the Goban Spur margin is almost devoid of canyons and inclined at about 1°. The continental slope of the Western Approaches margin, which forms the south-western limit of the report area, is incised by a complex of canyons and has an intermediate angle of slope. The abrupt changes in the morphology of the slope are coincident with, and related to, major changes in the geological structure of the margin (Avedik, 1975). The base of the slope at about 4500 m is approximately coincident with the boundary between oceanic and continental crust (Roberts et al., 1981).

The topographic framework of the slope was formed during the Early Cretaceous rifting episode; subsequently the outer continental margin (slope and outer shelf) subsided with a magnitude which decreased with time so that the slope had nearly reached its present depth by the mid-Tertiary (Montadert et al., 1979). Sediment accumulation since the Early Cretaceous has not completely buried the fault-block topography produced during rifting, and the slope is typical of a margin 'starved' of sediment. The rotated fault-blocks do not extend landward to underlie the upper slope, whose present bathymetric form is the result of a balance between the constructional advance of the shelf edge and erosion by density currents and slumping.

The upper slope is underlain by a laterally irregular lens of Pliocene to Pleistocene sediment (lower Little Sole Formation) which thins rapidly both landward onto the outermost shelf and oceanward below a depth of about 1500 m (Figure 14). Prior to the last episode of major canyon cutting, the lens formed a continuous along-slope drape (Pinot, 1974), but the canyons on the upper slope carved through it into the underlying Tertiary and Mesozoic strata. The canyons are irregularly distributed on the upper slope of the Western Approaches margin, although on the Bay of Biscay margin they are more regularly spaced every 10 to 15 km. They feed into the

larger, irregularly orientated, middle and lower slope canyons whose positions are largely governed by the uncovered fault-blocks.

GLORIA long-range sidescan sonar images (Kenyon et al., 1978) show the canyon heads on the upper slope to have a steep-rimmed 'amphitheatre' shape composed of a series of leaf-like elements which merge down into the main canyon. Primary and secondary gullies cover their flanks and the canyons are normally V-shaped, though U-shaped profiles also occur, especially near the bottom of the slope (Figure 12b). Seismic profiles show levee-like bodies a few hundred metres across and about 50 m high perched at the top of some canyon rims. The canyon interfluves are either sharp-crested 'arêtes' or portions of undissected continental slope (Figure 12b and e). The canyon axes vary from straight to sinuous, with frequent sharp turns in their middle and lower courses, and the canyons coalesce downwards to produce a dendritic pattern. The true complexity of this slope is apparent from the limited number of detailed surveys carried out using the multibeam bathymetric system Sea-Beam (Pastouret et al., 1982); some of the slopes are intensely slumped and topographically complex, whereas others are simpler and rounded in form.

Where the upper slope is not incised by canyons (Figure 12e), there is a smooth increase in sea-bed inclination between depths of about 180 and 300 m. Seismic profiles show an increase in the continuity and amplitude of the reflectors within the Little Sole Formation below a water depth of 250 to 300 m. This change in reflector character corresponds to the lithological change from sandy sediments on the shelf to muddier sediments on the slope, and equates with the 'mud-line' described by Stanley et al. (1983). Slumping of surface units on and within the interfluves below a water depth of about 750 m has formed isolated lens-like bodies on the canyon walls that are up to a few hundred metres across and about 50 m thick. Slumped masses also occur within the upper 100 to 200 m of the Pliocene to Pleistocene cover, and the bounding basal listric surfaces of some are incipient fault planes.

The upper slope canyons were eroded during the Pleistocene after the deposition of the lower Little Sole Formation. Episodic low stands of sea level during this time led to intensification of wave and tidal action across the outer shelf and the transport of greater volumes of sand across the shelfbreak. Some of this sand may have formed into downslope density currents. Although the original along-slope surface form of the Little Sole Formation appears to have been smooth, it is likely that there

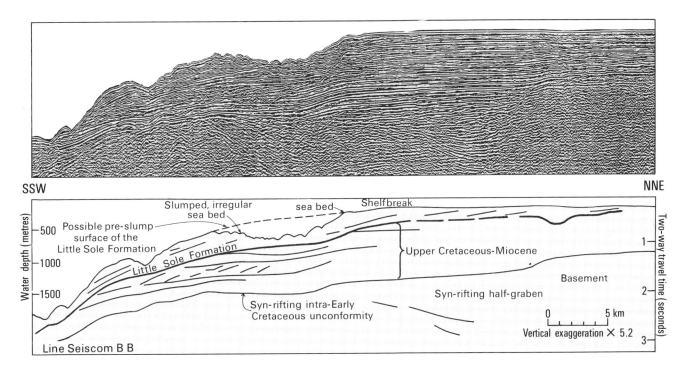

Figure 14 Seismic profile across the upper continental slope and outer shelf. For location see Figure 6.

were gentle undulations in its upper surface that would have been greatest above buried canyons or depressions where postdepositional compaction produced slight negative features. Density currents flowing over the shelfbreak would gravitate into these features and canyon cutting would commence precisely above the sites of the earlier incisions, to produce nested canyons (Figure 15).

Density currents primarily cut into the floor of the canyons, and slumping of the subsequently oversteepened canyon walls is the principal mechanism for their enlarge-

ment. The gulleys presently covering the canyon sides cannot be due to density currents flowing off the shelf, for they terminate against the interfluves and do not link back into the shelf. There is no evidence for modern major slumping on the upper slope, though minor transport probably occurs along the canyon floors, especially following storms (Mart et al., 1979). However, the incision by backwall erosion of a canyon into a tidal sand ridge near the shelfbreak (Figure 12a) is evidence for slumping on the slope since the last glacial maximum.

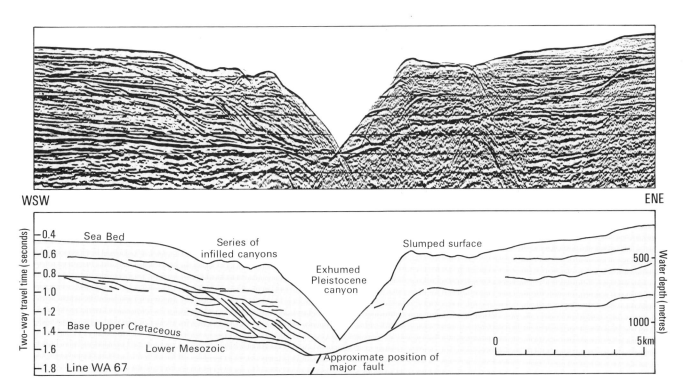

Figure 15 Seismic section across the upper continental slope showing an exhumed canyon. For location see Figure 6.

15

3 Crustal structure

The lithosphere is divided by the Mohorovičić Discontinuity (Moho) into the crust and upper mantle. The Moho is a major seismic discontinuity across which the velocity increases downwards from an average crustal velocity of about 6.20 km/s to some 8.07 km/s at the top of the upper mantle (Holder and Bott, 1971). Recent seismic profiling techniques (BIRPS and ECORS, 1986) have enabled geophysicists to image reflections from the continental lithosphere below the Moho, which in this area lies some 30 kms below the surface of the earth. The only real seismic events imaged beneath the Moho in the report area may be the tectonic discontinuities or shear zones in the upper mantle recognised on SWAT line 8 in the eastern part of the Western Approaches Trough and on SWAT line 4 in the Celtic Sea (McGeary and Warner, 1985; BIRPS and ECORS, 1986).

From the BIRPS profiles, a tripartite seismic subdivision of the crust is recognised (Figure 16):
1. The lower crust is highly reflective, and its base is correlated with the Moho on the basis of the velocity changes recognised at the same level from refraction experiments (Holder and Bott, 1971; Barton et al., 1984).
2. The middle crust is generally featureless, though traversed by dipping reflectors produced by thrust or fault planes.
3. The upper crust, which does not always occur, forms a complex reflective unit that corresponds to the post-Carboniferous sedimentary cover.

The lower and middle crust are formed of Late Carboniferous and older metamorphic and igneous rocks that are collectively described in this report as the basement; the geometry of the post-Carboniferous sequences preserved in the sedimentary basins has been strongly influenced by the structure of the underlying basement.

CRUSTAL THICKNESS

Worzel (1968), using pendulum gravity observations, estimated that the crust under the shelf near south-west England was about 26 km thick. In 1966, three lines were shot radiating from Land's End in a seismic refraction experiment to investigate the structure of the crust across the region (Bott et al., 1970; Holder and Bott, 1971). Line 1 followed the Cornubian Batholith west-south-west as far as 49°N 8°40′W, and the other two lines extended towards Ireland and Brittany respectively. The crust under line 1 was consistently about 27 km thick, and the mean crustal velocity was estimated to be 6.20 km/s. These values suggest that a seismic velocity of 6.0 km/s is reasonable for time to depth conversion of crustal sections in BIRPS profiles from the region, taking into account the cover of lower velocity Permian and younger rocks. Results from lines 2 and 3 suggest that the Moho is not significantly warped under the sedimentary basins which they cross.

A more recent refraction experiment (Avedik et al., 1982; Ginzburg et al., 1985) on the edge of the continental shelf crossed the Shelf Edge Basin, the western part of the Melville Basin and the intervening basement high (Figure 4). The results show a p-wave velocity increase from 6.6 to 8.0 km/s related to the Moho at a depth of 36 km, but the interpretation did not take into account variations in the signal delay due to the sedimentary cover.

The acquisition of seismic reflection profiles which image reflections at least down to the base of the crust (BIRPS and ECORS, 1986) has allowed a more continuous assessment of crustal thickness than is possible with refraction experiments. The western end of the BIRPS WAM line shows the Moho under the outermost continental shelf at a depth of 33 km (11 seconds TWTT) rising oceanward to a depth of about 12 km (8.5 seconds TWTT) at the oceanic–continental crust transition (Pinet et al., 1987). Meissner et al. (1986), using both reflection and refraction data, show the Moho across the region as a subhorizontal surface undulating gradually from a depth of slightly greater than 30 km to less than 25 km (Figure 17).

The Moho surface is not disrupted by major Caledonian or Variscan structures, though it retains a 'memory' of Mesozoic and Tertiary processes (Meissner et al., 1986). An example of this is a 3 km rise in the level of the Moho under the Plymouth Bay Basin which contains about 8 km of Permo-Triassic sediment beneath which the crystalline basement is reduced in thickness to about 21 km (BIRPS and ECORS, 1986). The rise in the Moho under the basin is a result of the crust maintaining isostatic equilibrium, and compensating for the thick sequence of lighter upper crust sediments by a rise in the underlying denser mantle (Figure 18). The thicknesses shown in Figure 18 differ slightly from those of BIRPS and ECORS (1986) because different velocities have been used to convert the time-based seismic sections to true depth.

LOWER CRUST

The lower crust is equated with a zone of subhorizontal reflectors seen extensively on BIRPS seismic lines which traverse the continental shelf around the UK (McGeary et al., 1987; Peddy and Hobbs, 1987). In the North Sea, the base of this reflective zone has been shown to coincide with the Moho as defined from refraction experiments (Barton et al., 1984), a correlation that is extended to the study region. The reflectors under the Cornubian Platform, which can be traced laterally for up to 25 km, are very bright and subhorizonal, or less coherent, diffractive events (Peddy and Hobbs, 1987). Off south-west Britain, the lower crust usually extends from a depth of about 18 to 24 km (6 to 8 seconds TWTT) down to the Moho at some 30 km (10 seconds TWTT), and the thickness of the zone remains approximately constant over large distances. Both the amplitude and coherence of the reflections increase towards the base of the crust and terminate with a bright Moho event (Cheadle et al., 1987), although these are not clearly imaged in Figure 16.

Under the Haig Fras granite on SWAT line 5, the top of the lower crustal reflectors rises from a regional depth of about 8 seconds (TWTT) to some 5 seconds (TWTT). On SWAT line 6 there is a similar, though less prominent, rise

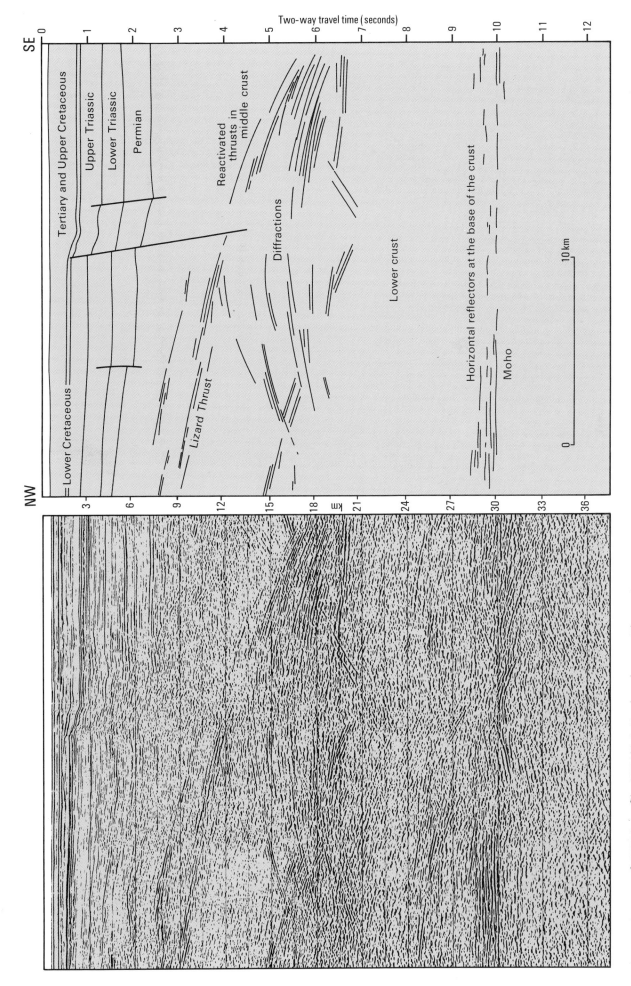

Figure 16 Part of BIRPS profile SWAT 6. For location see Figure 6.

17

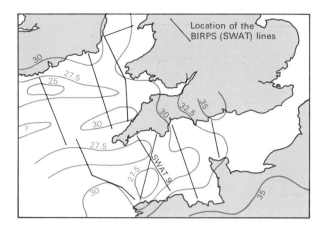

Figure 17 Depth of the Moho across the region in kilometres. Taken from Meissner et al. (1986).

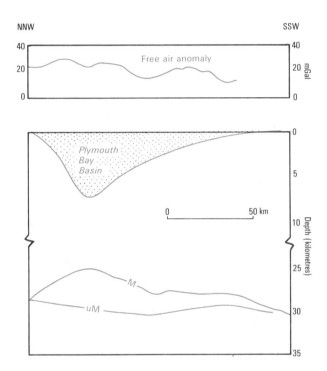

Figure 18 Geophysical profile across the Plymouth Bay Basin from SWAT line 9.

This figure shows the relationship between the free air gravity anomaly and depth to the Moho, both corrected (M) and uncorrected (uM) for velocity changes in the upper crust. Note the break in the depth scale between 10 km and 25 km. Location of SWAT line 9 is shown in Figure 6. Redrawn from Meissner et al. (1986).

under the Cornubian Batholith near the Isles of Scilly where an isolated event at about 10.5 km (3.5 seconds TWTT) may correspond to the base of the batholith (Matthews, 1987).

On the WAM profile, the characteristic lower crustal reflectors are recognised along the eastern part of the line immediately west of the Isles of Scilly, but fade gradually where the line crosses the Fastnet Basin. The reflectors reappear at the base of the continental slope with no recognisable change in style despite the extended, thinned nature of the crust at the continental margin (Peddy and Hobbs, 1987). This fading of the reflectors under the basin has been attributed to increased noise in the profiles from the upper part of the crust, but the abrupt truncation of the reflectors across a strike-slip fault under the basin

shows that their disappearance is in part real. Where the WAM and SWAT-5 lines intersect (Figure 6), the lower crustal reflectors dip gently to the west-south-west, the local direction of extension during the opening of the North Atlantic (Peddy and Hobbs, 1987).

The lateral uniformity of the reflectors in the lower crust under both basement and basinal areas suggested to Pinet et al. (1987) that the reshaping of the lower crust to produce these reflectors occurred after the last major thermal event to affect the zone. As the last major thermal event accompanied the crustal extension during the early Mesozoic, the reflectors are considered to postdate that event and may be of Jurassic age.

MIDDLE CRUST

The top of the lower crustal reflectors is the seismically defined junction between the lower and middle crust. It may correlate with the boundary between that lower portion of the crust which behaves in a ductile fashion during episodes of lithospheric extension, and the overlying part in which brittle deformation occurs (Peddy and Hobbs, 1987).

The middle crust is seismically almost featureless, but includes locally distinctive packets of semicontinuous dipping reflectors. This general absence of reflectors may be due to intense deformation which has reduced both the continuity of the reflectors and the impedance contrasts between lithologies (Cheadle et al., 1987). The packets of dipping events recognised in the middle crust of the Western Approaches by Hillis and Day (1987) appear approximately planar; their true dip is between 20° and 35° with a south-easterly strike parallel to the structural grain of the area (Figure 19). The reflections converge down-dip to merge with the top of the horizontal lower crustal reflectors at a depth of about 20 km (Holder and Leveridge, 1986a), leading Hillis and Day (1987) to interpret them as images of Variscan thrusts with detachment at the top of the lower crust. None of the fault plane reflections described by Hillis and Day (1987) or Cheadle et al. (1987) cut through the crust into the mantle. The reflectors are largely absent from areas enclosed by the 20 mGal Bouguer anomaly contour, which approximately follows the limits of the Variscan granites (Figure 19); this implies that such events are absent within the batholiths, which onshore are younger than the major Variscan thrusts.

Hendriks (1939) proposed that a line from Start Point through Dodman Point to the Lizard marks a relic boundary zone of a Variscan nappe. Recent work (Leveridge et al., 1984; Holder and Leveridge 1986a; 1986b) has shown that at least three laterally extensive nappe sheets of Devonian age are involved in the zone. The most northerly is the Carrick Nappe, overlain to the south by the Dodman and Lizard nappes. Seismic profiles located near to the coast have permitted the sequence of boundary thrusts separating the nappes in south Cornwall to be linked spatially with the offshore middle crust reflectors (Leveridge et al., 1984; Holder and Leveridge, 1986a). The seismic profiles indicate that the Carrick Nappe is between 10 and 12 km thick offshore, whereas onshore it is only about half this value. The basal thrusts to the Carrick and Lizard nappes have been traced offshore westwards to about 7°W; the Normannian Thrust, identified about 70 km south-east of the Isles of Scilly (Hillis, 1988), cannot be demonstrably linked with any structure to the east, though Holder and Leveridge (1986a) show the thrust as a major feature in their palaeotectonic reconstruction. Pinet

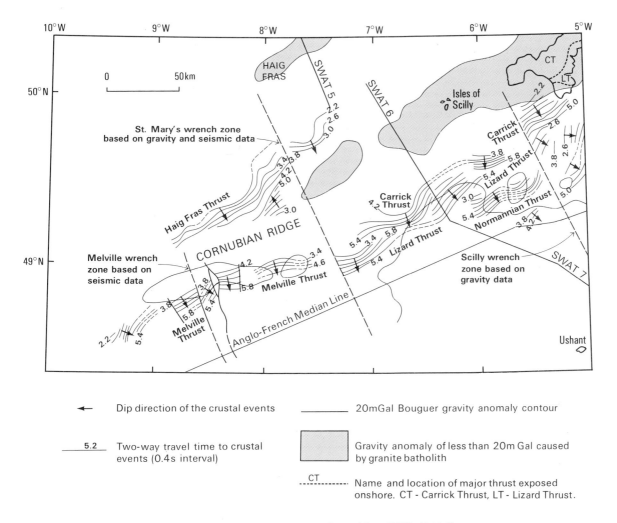

Figure 19 Deep crustal events in the Western Approaches. After Hillis (1988).

et al. (1987) show the Lizard Thrust (Front) extending unbroken along the northern part of the western English Channel and into the Western Approaches, though Hillis and Day (1987) do not show the feature having such lateral continuity. The thrust is imaged under the Plymouth Bay Basin where it may be amalgamated with adjacent thrusts. Here it is termed the Lizard Front, and cuts through the reflective lower crust but leaves it largely unaffected (Pinet et al., 1987). On SWAT line 6 to the south of the Isles of Scilly, the same feature, termed the Scilly Fault System by BIRPS and ECORS (1986) and the Lizard and Carrick thrusts by Hillis (1988), can be followed into the lower crust to a depth of at least 17 km (Figure 19).

UPPER CRUST

The grain of the post-Carboniferous rocks forming the upper crust was set by extension of the crust during Permo-Triassic and Late Jurassic to Early Cretaceous times, when reactivation of Variscan structures led to the formation of sedimentary basins. The location and geometry of the basins is thus intimately related to both the east-north-east-trending Variscan structures and the slightly later north-westerly aligned wrench faults.

Since the inception of the basins, the crust has been subjected to a number of extensional events interspersed with phases of minor compression and uplift, the effects of which are preserved in the stratigraphic records of the basins. During most periods of sedimentation, the plat-

forms and parts of the massifs were topographically low features on which a thin sedimentary cover accumulated, but subsequent uplift has led to erosion of most of these sequences to leave the Mesozoic and Tertiary strata confined largely to the offshore basins.

On the BIRPS seismic profiles, the basins forming the upper crust image as discrete, broad, sagged infills locally containing over 9 km of post-Upper Carboniferous sediment in which there are a number of regionally correlatable unconformities (Figure 8); the basins generally contain a fault-controlled lower sequence overlain by a more widespread upper sequence. The major basinal feature is the Western Approaches Trough, which is divided into a number of basins (Figure 4), each of which contains a slightly different stratigraphic record indicating variations in response to tectonic stresses.

North of the Western Approaches Trough is the parallel-trending Cornubian Ridge, a basement feature in part intruded by granite batholiths. The Armorican Massif and Armorican Platform make up the southern flank of the trough, and encroach into the report area only around the Channel Islands. The Western Approaches Trough is separated from the Portland–Wight Basin to the east by the Start–Cotentin Ridge, where basement shallows to less than 2 km below sea bed (Figure 4).

North of the Cornubian Platform is the South Celtic Sea Basin, whose southern portion forms the northernmost part of the report area. This basin extends north-eastwards into the Bristol Channel Basin (Figure 4).

4 Basement

The rocks within the area may be divided into two main units that pre- and postdate the Variscan orogeny. The two units are separated by a widespread unconformity, and this chapter deals with the rocks beneath the unconformity which form the basement to the overlying sedimentary basins. The basement crops out on the Cornubian Ridge and the Armorican Massif and Platform. The Cornubian Ridge forms the northern flank of the Western Approaches Trough and is composed of Devonian and Carboniferous rocks, whereas the Armorican Massif to the south of the trough in north-west France and the Channel Islands is formed of older Precambrian rocks with minor, discontinuous, Palaeozoic outliers and some Variscan intrusions.

The pre-Devonian palaeogeography of the region is uncertain, though the Ouessant–Alderney fault zone (Figure 4) may mark the boundary between predominantly Palaeozoic rocks to the north and Precambrian rocks to the south (Lefort and Segoufin, 1978). During Devonian and Carboniferous time an east–west-trending, southward-dipping subduction zone lay in an oceanic basin that occupied part of the western English Channel to the south of Cornwall. The tectonic events of this time are intimately linked with the closure of this oceanic basin and the subsequent continent–continent collision that produced the Variscan orogeny. In post-Namurian times, the main compressional phase of the Variscan orogeny was more or less synchronous from southern Armorica to South Wales. During the final phase of the orogeny, granite batholiths were intruded into the Cornubian Ridge and high level plutons of the same age occur in Brittany and the Cotentin Peninsula.

Lithological data on pre-Permian basement rocks offshore are limited. Gravity coring and dredging of areas where the rocks are near sea bed have yielded the most samples, though divers have obtained specimens from the shallower reefs (Phillips, 1964), and some wells have terminated in basement. Seismic profiling rarely images continuous reflectors within the usually tectonised rocks because of the lack of acoustic impedance contrasts and the structural complexity of the strata. The extensively studied onshore sections in south-west England and Brittany provide the model used to interpret the limited suite of offshore data.

CORNUBIAN RIDGE

The Cornubian Ridge is composed principally of structurally complex clastic sequences of Devonian and Carboniferous age that were caught up in the Variscan orogeny when the sediments were compressed and intruded by granite batholiths.

Cope (1987) presents a conjectural pre-Devonian palaeogeological map of south-west England and its surrounds that shows most of the peninsula underlain by Precambrian metamorphic rocks, passing southwards at an arcuate line a little north of the Lizard and Start Point into Cambrian and Ordovician rocks. This southern boundary is located on the premise that Lower Palaeozoic rocks within the Gorran Quartzite are in situ (Sadler, 1973), a view challenged by Holder and Leveridge (1986a) who pro-

pose that they were tectonically transported from the south. Accepting the latter interpretation would place the Precambrian/Lower Palaeozoic boundary under Devonian strata in the English Channel, perhaps just north of the Eddystone Reef or along the Ouessant–Alderney fault zone (Lefort and Segoufin, 1978).

Ordovician and Silurian

Clasts of Ordovician quartzite and Silurian limestone are found in the Late Devonian Roseland Breccia Formation in south Cornwall, along with clasts of phyllite, schist, granite and quartzite comparable to the Brioverian and Palaeozoic sequences of Armorica (Holder and Leveridge, 1986a). Sadler (1973) considered the unit to be a condensed Ordovician to Middle Devonian sequence imbricated by tectonic deformation. Holder and Leveridge (1986a; 1986b) have reinterpreted it as a major olistostrome of wildflysch; a confused mass containing exotic blocks that slumped northwards into the trough from tectonically uplifted areas formed during the Late Devonian when thrust sheets encroached from the south.

Devonian

The Devonian strata in south-west England were deposited in a basin situated between the Normannian High (Ziegler, 1982) to the south and the margins of Laurentia to the north (Holder and Leveridge, 1986a). The Normannian High was located in the western English Channel; during the Early Devonian, sediment was shed southwards from it into Brittany and northwards into Cornwall.

Shallow-water sedimentation accompanied by isolated vulcanicity spread into Cornwall from the south-west during the Early Devonian. Several hundred metres of mudstone with siltstone and sandstone were deposited, as well as isolated fishbone beds up to a metre thick. During the Middle Devonian, shallow-marine clastic sedimentation with volcanism and reefal development characterised much of the peninsula, interdigitating with a terrestrial facies in the far north in front of the northward-advancing nappe complex. To the south, deep-water greywacke and mudstone with sporadic limestone, lava and conglomerate were deposited. All these rocks were caught up in the deformation related to Late Devonian nappe formation and the Late Carboniferous Variscan orogeny.

Deeper-water conditions migrated north in front of the northward-advancing nappe complex, and wildflysch sedimentation reached a climax in south Cornwall in the Late Devonian. The closure of this oceanic basin in south Cornwall during the Late Devonian produced a series of southward-dipping thrust nappes, one of which, the Lizard Nappe, obducted a slice of the ocean floor (the Lizard Complex) over the deep-water marine sequences (Leveridge et al., 1984).

Lizard Complex

The Lizard Complex (Figure 3) is an ophiolite; a fragment of oceanic lithosphere thrust onto the continental crust of south Cornwall as a result of tectonic processes at the margin of converging plates, probably during the Late Devonian (Styles and Rundle, 1984). Refraction experiments have shown that the complex is a sheet approximately 1 km thick underlain by about 3 km of Devonian metasediments and metavolcanics that pass down into pre-Devonian crystalline basement (Doody and Brooks, 1986). The basal contact of the complex along its northern outcrop is a thrust that is recognised, at the surface, for only a short distance offshore.

The Lizard Complex consists of a body of peridotite about 10 km in diameter largely surrounded by amphibolite and intruded by gabbros, basic dykes and granite veins (Leake and Styles, 1984). The mafic rocks have the chemistry of oceanic tholeiites (Badham, 1982). An Sm-Nd mineral isochron age of 375 ± 34 Ma (Middle to Late Devonian) was obtained from olivine gabbro within the complex, and obduction followed within a few million years of its formation (Davies, 1984).

The rocks around Eddystone Reef, Start Point and Dodman Point

The schists and gneiss exposed around Eddystone Reef, Start Point and Dodman Point are unlike other rocks in south-west England, and their structural position is enigmatic. The Eddystone Reef is an isolated pinnacle of garnetiferous, granitoid gneiss in Plymouth Bay that is part of a larger submarine outcrop of mica schist and granitoid gneiss surrounded by Permo-Triassic sediments (Figure 3). Isotopic age determinations suggest that the rocks were last deformed towards the end of the Devonian (375 Ma), but their highly metamorphosed state may indicate the effects of earlier, probably Precambrian, orogenic movements (Phillips, 1964; Edmonds et al., 1975).

Schists at Start Point (Figure 2) are faulted against the Lower Devonian Meadfoot Beds to the north. The schists extend offshore westwards to the West Rutts Reef, and southwards they are overlain by Triassic strata (Figure 3). The main rock types are green hornblende and chlorite schists and mica schists, with pink dolomitised limestone forming part of the East Rutts Reef (Phillips, 1964). They display similar structures to the Meadfoot Beds and have been considered to be tectonically altered Devonian rocks buried to greater depths than the adjacent Devonian rocks, and elevated by later normal faulting (Coward and McClay, 1983; Edmonds et al., 1975). The slightly metamorphosed subgreywackes and slates at Dodman Point closely resemble the Gramscatho Beds, and are faulted against Devonian breccias and conglomerates (Edmonds et al., 1975).

Doody and Brooks (1986) identified a refractor with a velocity of 6.09 km/s near the Eddystone Reef at a depth of less than a kilometre; this is probably the top of the metamorphic rocks that are exposed at the reef. The refractor is also identified at a depth of about 4 km under the Lizard, rising eastwards to reach the surface a short distance to the west of Start Point. These refraction data suggest that the exposed metamorphic rocks at the two localities are part of the pre-Devonian crystalline basement.

The structural position of these inliers and the Lizard Complex is best interpreted in terms of the Devonian tectonic history proposed by Holder and Leveridge (1986 a). The Eddystone rocks are probably a Precambrian remnant of the continental margin of the oceanic Cornwall Basin that was remetamorphosed during the Devonian. The Lizard ophiolite is thrust over a metasedimentary and metavolcanic sequence that, like the greenschists at Start Point, has an ocean-floor geochemical signature (Rice-

Birchall and Floyd, 1988). Both were probably deposited in the Cornwall Basin which formed during the Late Silurian to Early Devonian (Franke et al., 1989); thus the rocks of Start Point and Dodman Point are no older. The interpretation of the refraction data proposed by Doody and Brooks (1986) may reflect the physical characteristics of the rocks, but not their age.

Carboniferous

Carboniferous strata, known as the Culm Measures, occupy the core of an east–west-trending synclinorium which stretches on land from the west coast of Devon to the eastern side of Dartmoor (Figure 3). The Lower Carboniferous rocks that form a narrow belt along both flanks of the synclinorium are composed of dark grey shale with thin sandstone and mudstone beds as well as minor volcanic rocks, limestone and chert. The Namurian Crackington Formation at the base of the Upper Carboniferous consists of shale with thin turbiditic sandstone beds, and the overlying Bude Formation is made up of thick sandstone interbedded with shale. The youngest pre-orogenic sediments in the area are part of this formation and are of early Westphalian age.

Quiescent, shallow-marine conditions prevailed during the Early Carboniferous, but towards the end of this time, sedimentation was accompanied by igneous activity as the basin became increasingly influenced by the northward encroachment of the tectonically produced high which had affected Cornwall during the Devonian. Viséan flysch and olistostromic sequences were generated ahead of the advancing deformation front which formed submarine rises that were subject to erosion and slumping. These events heralded the beginning of the Variscan orogeny across the basin. With the closure of the basin during the Westphalian, shallow-water sequences again accumulated across the area (Isaac et al., 1982), and continued compression deformed these sediments during the final stages of the Variscan orogeny.

ARMORICAN MASSIF

The Channel Islands, the main islands of which are Jersey, Guernsey, Alderney and Sark, are part of the Armorican Massif (Figures 1 and 4). The islands are composed of Precambrian rocks intruded by igneous bodies and overlain unconformably by Lower Palaeozoic clastic sequences.

Precambrian

The Precambrian rocks of the massif are divisible into two units (Figure 5). The older, the Pentevrian, is well exposed on Guernsey and Alderney and comprises granitic and quartz-dioritic orthogneiss, schist and amphibolite deformed during the Icartian (2700 to 2550 Ma) and the Lihouan (2000 to 1900 Ma) orogenic episodes (Roach et al., 1972). The younger unit, the Brioverian, rests unconformably on the Pentevrian and consists of a turbiditic sequence of mudstone, siltstone and greywacke (Jersey Shale Formation) overlain by andesitic and acidic lava and tuff (Volcanic Group of Helm, 1984). Deposition of the Brioverian sedimentary cycle spanned the interval between 1000 and 650 Ma (Adams, 1976).

These rocks were later deformed during the Cadomian orogeny between 690 and 570 Ma; the main, predominantly greenschist, metamorphic event was between 620 and 650 ma when the rocks were folded into north-east- to east-trending structures with a penetrative foliation. Granites, granodiorites, diorites and gabbros, were emplaced both before and after the main metamorphic event. An additional, post-tectonic granite phase, ranging from 530 to 480 Ma is recognised on Jersey (Adams, 1976) and along the southern side of the Ouessant–Alderney fault zone (Lefort and Segoufin, 1978).

The northern, near-surface limit of the Armorican Platform lies along the Ouessant–Alderney fault zone, just north of a line from Alderney to Ushant, where the basement is both faulted against, and overlain by, Mesozoic and Tertiary strata (Figure 3).

Cambrian

On Alderney, metamorphic rocks dating from the Cadomian orogeny are overlain unconformably by the Alderney Sandstone which is nearly 800 m thick and consists of red and yellow arkosic sandstone with rare siltstone (Rathan, 1983). The Rozel Conglomerate on Jersey occupies a similar structural position and is probably of the same age. The conglomerate is cut by a hornblende lamprophyre with a minimum age of 427 Ma, but the age of the Alderney Sandstone is not so well defined (Renouf, 1974). The sediments were laid down as alluvial fans, probably during the Early Cambrian (Doré, 1972), after the terminal stage of Cadomian granite emplacement (Sutton and Watson, 1970).

Ordovician to Carboniferous

A number of minor outliers of Palaeozoic rock occur in Brittany, but no sediments younger than Early Cambrian are found on the Channel Islands. The Arenig Grès Armoricain orthoquartzites and the Llanvirn Schistes à Calymènes are part of the same province as the contemporaneous deposits in the Welsh Basin. The succeeding strata of Llandeilo age are lithologically similar to the Gorran Quartzites in south Cornwall. A submarine outcrop of Silurian strata has been described by Deunff et al. (1971) on the southern margin of the Minquiers between St Malo and Jersey (Figure 1).

The flysch-like Schistes et Quartzites laid down in north-west France at the close of the Silurian and the beginning of the Devonian were derived from a northerly source in the English Channel. They mark the onset of tectonic instability and increasing emergence during the Middle and Late Devonian. The earliest marine shales, of Late Devonian age, were deposited in small basins with shifting loci of sedimentation; where such sedimentation persisted it became dominated by coarse, terrestrially derived material.

In Normandy and east of Douarnenez near Brest (Renouf, 1974), small outcrops of lower Westphalian rocks are found in one outlier, and postorogenic Stephanian strata are preserved in intermontane basins.

OFFSHORE RESULTS

Eight offshore wells or boreholes in the region have penetrated Palaeozoic or Precambrian rocks, and samples of similar rocks have been recovered from the sea bed using gravity corers in the coastal zone and around Haig Fras (BGS Solid Geology sheets). Dredging of the continental slope has also yielded Palaeozoic rocks (Auffret et al., 1979). However, the samples sites are widely spaced and the results cannot be correlated into a regional synthesis.

Well 73/2-1, drilled on the outer shelf in the western part of the Melville Basin (Figure 7), terminated in 64 m of amphibolite-granulite gneiss. The upper 11 m has the appearance of a reworked conglomerate. The terminal core was dated using K-Ar as 570 ± 10 Ma, which suggests a correlation with the Cadomian rocks of the Armorican Massif.

Well Lennket-1, in the Southwest Channel Basin, terminated at a depth of 2762 m in 72 m of monzonite containing microcline and sericitised plagioclase. The rock is partly gneissose with a porphyroblastic or granulitic texture.

Well 83/24-1 (Figure 8), drilled on the south-western flank of the Cornubian Platform, terminated in 140 m of reddish brown to greyish black slate and mudstone with beds of hard, medium-grained mudstone of possible Devonian age. Quartz and calcite veins are common, and the mudstone is in part cherty (Evans et al., 1981).

Well 86/18-1, south of the Lizard, proved 109 m of dark grey to black, carbonaceous, siliceous shale with some chert. The unit is horizontally bedded, with some quartz veining and calcite-filled fractures. The presence of carbonaceous fragments in the overlying basal Permian conglomerates, and the carbonaceous character of the underlying shale, suggest that the latter may be equivalent to the postorogenic Upper Carboniferous in north-west France. However, the absence of conglomerates and coal in the section, and their cherty character, points to an Early Carboniferous or possibly Devonian age.

The basal section of well 87/12-1A, south-south-east of the Lizard, proved 479 m of Middle Devonian strata, the lower 312 m of which are of Eifelian to Givetian age. The basal part of this section consists of 17 m of fine-grained, lithic sandstone that passes up into 122 m of interbedded, black, fissile mudstone and lithic sandstone. The bulk of the overlying section is made up of a 324 m-thick, white to grey, Givetian biosparite with abundant macrofossils and calcite-filled fractures. At the top of the Devonian section is a 4 m-thick, purple to red mudstone passing up into a 12 m-thick, fine-grained, massive, lithic sandstone overlain by a basal Permian conglomerate. This upper shallow-water Devonian sequence may have developed on the southern flank of the basin in which the deep-water Gramscatho Group was accumulating to the north.

At site SLS 66, south-west of the Lizard, the section from 29.0 m below sea bed to the bottom of the hole at 93.0 m consists of grey, soft phyllite with irregular, hard laminations of grey or white shale and silt. Scattered pyrite is found, and the beds are folded. The rock is devoid of palynomorphs but is lithologically similar to the Devonian rocks of Cornwall.

Well 93/6-1, drilled on the southern margin of the South Celtic Sea Basin, bottomed in a 150 m thick Westphalian section that consists of black slate with thin quartz and calcite veins, and an uppermost 13 m of waxy, dark brown shale.

DSDP site 548 on the Goban Spur margin terminated in grey, unfossiliferous, fine-grained quartzite and black, shiny shale of Middle Devonian age. At site 549, the basal unit is a brown to grey, fine- to medium-grained, laminated sandstone of a terrestrial Old Red Sandstone facies. Muscovite from this facies yielded an age of about 700 Ma, which may reflect derivation from Cadomian basement. The good state of preservation of microfossils suggests that no important Palaeozoic metamorphism affected these rocks, thus the main metamorphic belt related to the Variscan orogeny is presumed to have lain to the south (Lefort et al., 1985).

Dredging and gravity coring of the Palaeozoic rocks

surrounding the Haig Fras granite has yielded soft, grey slate/phyllite of probable Devonian to Carboniferous age in which two sets of cleavage are sporadically recognised (Smith et al., 1965). Sampling the moderately rough sea bed to the north and west of the Cornubian Massif produced slate and phyllite with some coarser sediments and igneous rocks. To the south of Devon and Cornwall, igneous or metamorphosed rocks such as Eddystone Reef and Wolf Rock form upstanding shoals. Phillips (1963) describes a variety of rocks including schists and limestones dredged and recovered by divers from an area in Plymouth Bay between Eddystone Reef and East Rutts Reef (Figure 2).

Dredging from the continental slope has yielded a variety of Palaeozoic rocks (Auffret et al., 1979; Lefort et al., 1985), including granulite and charnockite from around Granite Cliff (Figure 1) (Didier et al., 1977). Chloritic schist has been dredged from the southern end of the Pendragon Escarpment, as have shallow-water, dark, biomicritic limestones of possible Viséan age. Variscan igneous rocks exposed on the south side of Goban Spur around Granite Cliff (Auffret et al., 1979) are described on p.27.

The scarcity of Palaeozoic and Precambrian samples away from the coastal zone precludes subdivision of the basement under the Western Approaches Trough, although the extent of the Variscan batholiths is discussed later. However, the Cadomian gneiss in well 73/2-1, the metamorphosed monzonite in well Lennket-1, and the schists of the Eddystone Rocks are all Precambrian rocks lying well to the north of the Ouessant–Alderney fault zone, and may have been brought to their present elevated structural level along Variscan thrusts. A south-south-easterly dipping event mapped in the vicinity of well 73/2-1, and interpreted as a thrust by Hillis and Day (1987), may have elevated the gneiss in the well to its present position.

VARISCAN OROGENY

During the Late Silurian to Early Devonian, the continents of Laurentia/Greenland and Fennoscandia/Baltica collided, forming the Caledonian mountains across much of Britain, Ireland, Newfoundland and the northern Appalachians. To the south of this newly formed Laurasian landmass lay the Proto-Tethys or Rheic Ocean; beyond it was Gondwana, from which microcontents began to break away and drift northwards to attach themselves to the southern margin of Laurasia. The northward movement of Gondwana, that led to the closure of the Rheic Ocean, began during the Devonian. Continent-to-continent collision between Gondwana and Laurasia began during the late Viséan to Namurian and formed the supercontinent of Pangaea (Ziegler, 1982). This collision caused the Variscan orogeny.

The report area lay on the southern flank of Laurasia, some distance north of the Rheic Ocean. During the Early Devonian, an elongate tensional back-arc basin, termed the Variscan Foredeep Basin, extended from southern Ireland to Poland. The section of the Foredeep Basin within the report area was the Cornwall Basin that lay to the north of the Normannian High (Ziegler, 1982) and ran approximately from the Channel Isles to west of the Isles of Scilly. The occurrence of the Lizard Complex (composed of oceanic tholeiites) indicates that the basin had a floor of oceanic crust, and Holder and Leveridge (1986b) propose that there was a southward-dipping subduction zone within the basin along the northern margin of the Normannian High during Devonian time. The Cornwall Basin was fed by sediment shed from both the Caledonian mountains to the north and the rising Normannian High to the south. The Normanian High was the surface expression of a thrust nappe that supplied fresh sediment to basins both to the north and south; the weight of the northward-moving nappe depressed the crust to the north to produce a foredeep basin. Deep-water conditions prevailed along the southern margin of this basin, the axis of which moved northwards with time. The stratigraphic development of the basin during the Devonian and Carboniferous was governed by the northward progression of the nappe complex; as it moved northwards, younger sediments became caught up in the tectonism and metamorphosed (Dodson and Rex, 1971). The slates in south Cornwall were metamorphosed between 365 and 345 Ma (Late Devonian), whereas metamorphism affecting the Carboniferous sediments in the core of the major syncline in Devon is dated between 340 and 260 Ma (Early Carboniferous to Late Permian).

The east-north-east-striking thrusts that formed during the Devonian and Carboniferous as a result of the closure of the Cornwall Basin are cut by a series of south-south-east-trending strike-slip faults which may have been initiated as lateral ramps to the thrusts and reactivated by later stresses (Coward and Smallwood, 1984). However, Ziegler (1982) proposed that the faults were formed in response to dextral shearing following a change in regional stresses during the later stages of the Variscan orogeny. Badham (1982) argues that these faults were boundaries to microplates on the southern margin of Laurasia that played an important part in the development of the area throughout the Late Palaeozoic.

Offshore, the location of the strike-slip faults is highlighted by gravity and magnetic anomalies (Figures 20 and 21), and Figures 4 and 19 show the probable trace of some of these structures, the best known of which is the Sticklepath–Lustleigh Fault which was probably active during the Variscan orogeny (Holloway and Chadwick, 1986). Holder and Leveridge (1986b) and Day (1986) proposed a 400 km dextral offset of the Variscan zone of Germany along one of these strike-slip faults, namely the Bristol Channel–Bray Fault (Figure 4) which is well defined in north-west France but not so readily identifiable in southern England. The apparent western termination of the Haig Fras and Cornubian batholiths at a north-west-trending gravity lineament between 49°20′N 7°42′W and 50°00′N 8°14′W (Figure 20) may be due to another large strike-slip offset in the basement. However, no extension of the batholiths has been recognised to the west of the lineament. Alternatively, the injection of the granites may have been limited to the zone between the Bristol Channel–Bray Fault and the fault marked by this lineament (Figure 4).

Movements during the suturing phase of the Pangaean megacontinent caused the fragmentation of the Variscan fold belt. By the end of the Carboniferous, the crust was a complex of major blocks defined by the Late Palaeozoic thrusts, their associated nappes, and the strike-slip faults. This framework controlled subsequent tectonic movement, including the inititiation of sedimentary basins during the Permian and crustal extension during the Triassic.

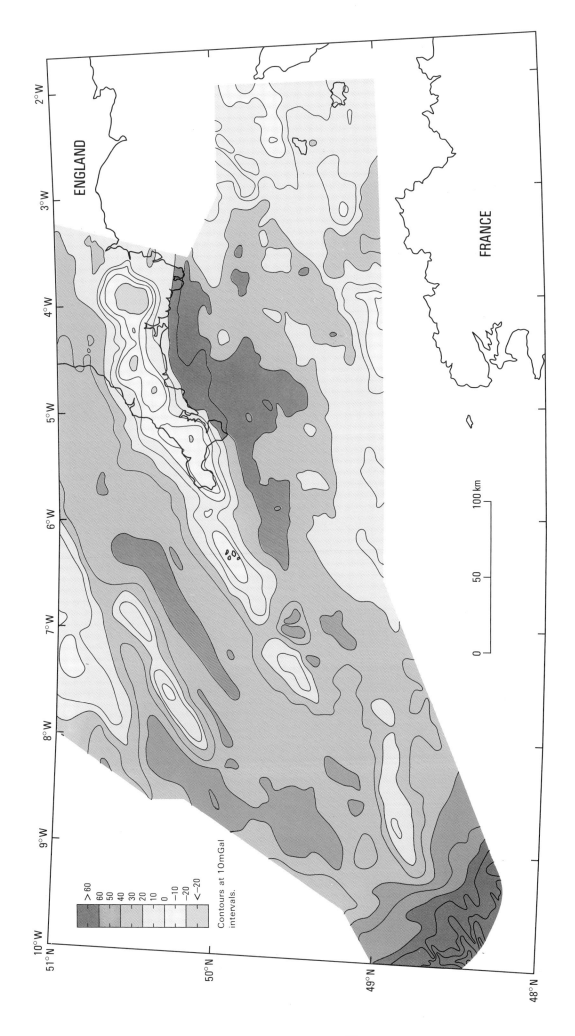

Figure 20 Bouguer gravity anomaly map of the report area.

ENGLAND

FRANCE

Contours at 10mGal
intervals.

> 60
60
50
40
30
20
10
0
−10
−20
< −20

24

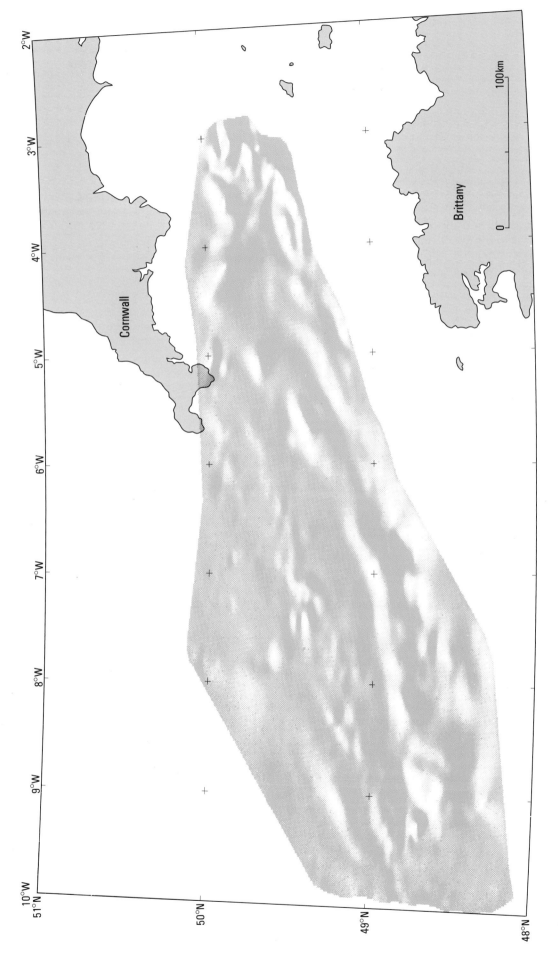

Figure 21 A computer-generated shaded relief map of aeromagnetic data from part of the area.

The map was produced by treating the data as a topographic relief surface illuminated from the north-west at an elevation of 30°.

25

VARISCAN IGNEOUS ROCKS

VARISCAN BATHOLITHS

In the Early Permian, during the closing stages of the Variscan orogeny and following the major thrusting episode, at least two major batholiths were intruded into the deformed Late Palaeozoic strata. Granite batholiths are associated with compressional tectonics and subduction zones, and the trend of the batholiths in this region is consistent with the north-north-westerly closure of the Variscan Foredeep Basin. The best known is the Cornubian Batholith which is exposed in a series of inliers from Dartmoor to the Isles of Scilly. A second parallel batholith offshore is centred under Haig Fras. The granites were intruded more or less contemporaneously with the extrusive Exeter Volcanic Series (Warrington and Scrivener, 1988) and the thick postorogenic volcanic pile in the Melville Basin. Onshore the batholith underlies the volcanics, but no Variscan granite underlies the Melville Basin.

The culmination of the Variscan orogeny and the intrusion of the granites produced an area with some considerable relief which was rapidly eroded. The occurrence of granite clasts in the Teignmouth Breccia Formation of Devon indicates that the unroofing of the granites had begun by Late Permian time, a process that continued until the Early Cretaceous (Edmonds et al., 1975).

Shackleton et al. (1982) considered that the present 27 km-thick crust in the vicinity of the granites was not thick enough to allow the generation of granitic magma by melting of the underlying crust. However, during the late stages of the Variscan orogeny the crust may have been up to 10 km thicker (Lake and Karner, 1987). Shackleton et al. (1982) proposed that the granites were generated farther south and injected northwards as a sheet-like body from which protrusions moved up diapirically and by stoping to form separate granite masses.

Cornubian Batholith

The Cornubian Batholith crops out discontinuously on land from Dartmoor to the Isles of Scilly (Figures 1 and 3) and is the cause of the negative gravity anomaly (Figure 20) over the Cornubian Peninsula (Bott et al., 1958). Tombs (1977) and Willis-Richards (1986) modelled the batholith using gravity data, and have shown that the outcrops are the tops of cupolas on a batholith which is continuous at depth. The batholith widens from about 10 km near surface to between 30 and 50 km at its base, which is placed at a depth of between 10 and 12 km.

The negative gravity anomaly (Figure 20) continues west-south-west from the Isles of Scilly as far as 7°45′W, and a two-dimensional gravity model incorporating seismic information shows that this anomaly is due to the offshore continuation of the batholith, and not to lighter sediments in the upper crust (Edwards, 1984). Seismic data suggest that the top of the body comes to within a few hundred metres of the sea bed about 100 km to the west-south-west of the Isles of Scilly (BGS Scilly Solid Geology sheet). The outline of the batholith, as traced by the gravity anomaly, has the appearance of being offset between the Isles of Scilly and the mainland, possibly the result of a major dextral shear fault (Figures 4 and 19).

Onshore, the Cornubian Batholith consists of coarse, adamellitic granite with tourmaline, zircon and apatite as the commonest accessory minerals (Edmonds et al., 1975). The chemical and mineralogical composition of the granites is generally uniform, although the Dartmoor granite is more acidic than the others. All the granites contain felsic veins and pods. Segregations of quartz-tourmaline rock are common, and dykes of this material traverse the country rock. Steep-sided elvans (quartz-porphyry dykes) up to 40 m across occur around the granites, and may have been feeders for subaerial vulcanicity.

According to Rb-Sr isotopic evidence, the batholith was emplaced between 290 and 280 Ma (Early Permian), with the main stage of polymetallic mineralisation at about 270 Ma (Darbyshire and Shepherd, 1985). This age is more constrained than the range of 303 to 254 Ma derived from K-Ar results (Edmonds et al., 1975) which reflect the cooling, rather than the emplacement of the intrusion (Darbyshire and Shepherd, 1985).

Haig Fras Batholith

The submarine shoal termed Haig Fras is an outcrop of granite lying some 150 km west of Land's End and rising up to 50 m above the surrounding sea bed. The exposed body is elongated in a north-easterly direction and measures about 45 by 15 km. Most samples of the granite have been collected by dredge, but some gravity cores have also been obtained (Smith et al., 1965; Exley, 1966; Jones et al., 1988). The commonest rock is a fine-grained, foliated, leucocratic and tourmaline-bearing granite of pale grey or buff colour. It is generally composed of irregular plates of potash feldspar (commonly microcline-perthite up to 3 mm across and oligoclase up to 1.5 mm across) in a groundmass of potash feldspar, quartz, oligoclase, and flakes of muscovite. Greenish brown tourmaline forms idiomorphic crystals, some with blue centres. Almandine garnet is plentiful in the microcline granite. The Haig Fras granite is more sodic than those on the mainland, and corresponds chemically with the leuco-granitic sheets and veins which intrude both the granite and country rock of the Cornubian Batholith. The granite has a K-Ar date of 277 Ma (Exley, 1966).

Sea-bed photographs of the granite surface show an irregular surface formed into rounded blocks up to some two metres across, with deeply weathered and enlarged joint planes. This topography is similar to that of the onshore granite tors, which suggests that the subsea features were formed during a glacial low stand or an earlier period of subaerial erosion.

Miller et al. (1977) and Jones et al. (1988) measured uranium, potassium and thorium values of the granite and country rock using a spectrometer towed along the sea bed (Figure 22). They recognised a granite made up of three separate outcrops, with the north-eastern body topographically more subdued than the others and displaying lower uranium and thorium counts. Similar radiological variations were obtained over the kaolinised and unaltered granites onshore, which may suggest that the lower relief of this part of the offshore batholith indicates a softer lithology due to partial kaolinisation of the rock.

Highly granitised or feldspathised schists with feldspar in irregular veins are associated with the granitic rocks. They contain porphyroblasts of microcline-microperthite up to 10 mm across set in a groundmass of microcline, quartz, oligoclase and biotite. In some schists, the feldspars occur in well-defined bands several millimetres thick, and tourmaline may be abundant. These schists were considered by Sabine (in Smith et al., 1965) to have been subjected to late-stage granitic permeation and metamorphism. There is also evidence of cataclastic deformation affecting the quartzofeldspathic groundmass. These

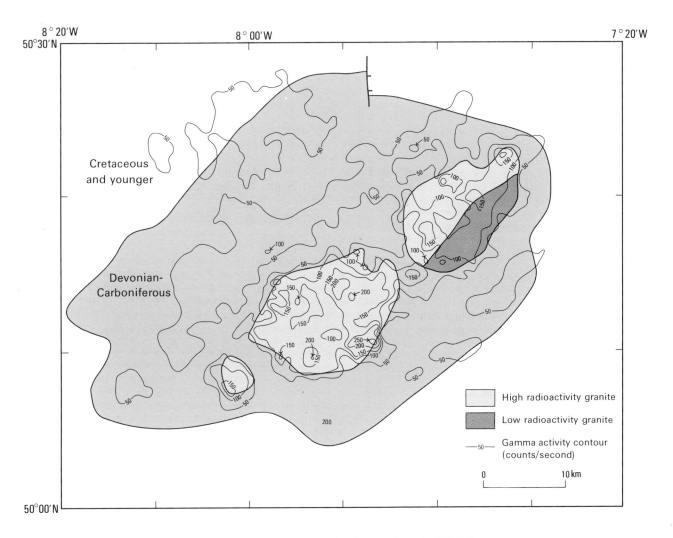

Figure 22 Geological map of Haig Fras, showing sea-bed radioactivity. Modified from Jones et al. (1988).

rocks are unlike the metamorphosed country rock in the aureole of the Cornubian Batholith and resemble the gneiss found on White Island on the Isles of Scilly, which has been interpreted as a sheared granite permeated by later growth of tourmaline and quartz.

Granites under the outer shelf and continental slope

The south-western limits of both the Haig Fras and Cornubian batholiths, as determined from gravity data, fall on a line extending from 49°2′N 7°42′W to 50°00′N 8°14′W (Figure 20). No granites are inferred from gravity and magnetic data to underlie the continental shelf to the west of this line. However, granitic rocks have been dredged from the lower continental slope to the south-west of the report area at a water depth of 3500 to 4000 m (Auffret et al., 1979). The dominant granite facies out-cropping on Granite Cliff (Figure 1) is a granodiorite which in some specimens has the composition of quartz-diorite or tonalite. The age of this rock using both Rb-Sr and K-Ar methods is 275 Ma (total rock) or 290 Ma (biotite). Its petrology and Early Permian age assign the granodiorite to the Variscan intrusive episode.

LATE CARBONIFEROUS AND EARLY PERMIAN VOLCANICS

Volcanic rocks associated with the basal postorogenic redbeds rest unconformably on tectonised basement rocks in the Melville Basin, and may occur in the Plymouth Bay Basin (Pinet et al., 1987). The Exeter Volcanic Series occupy the same stratigraphic position in eastern Devon, and form an analogue for the volcanic rocks in the offshore basin.

The Exeter Volcanic Series crop out in the Crediton Trough north of Dartmoor (Figure 3) and at, or near, the base of the Permian succession to the east of Dartmoor. They are a poorly exposed suite of vesicular and scoria-ceous, potash-rich lavas with subordinate olivine basalts. These remnants of a formerly more extensive sequence normally rest on Carboniferous strata, and some of the basal redbed breccias contain a range of igneous and tec-tonised rocks of that age. The lavas from Killerton have been K-Ar dated as 291 Ma (Late Carboniferous) by Thorpe et al. (1986) and 283±5 Ma (Early Permian) by Rundle (in Bristow et al., 1985). Lamprophyre dykes cut both the granites and country rocks, and may have been the feeders to the lavas (Durrance and Laming, 1982). These dykes and associated lavas have yielded a Stephanian mean age of 295 Ma (Rundle in Hawkes, 1981), a figure comparable with data from similar lamprophyre dykes in the Channel Islands and in Brittany (Lees, 1974). Taken together, the available stratigraphic and radiometric data indicate that the lavas were extruded at more than one period during the Stephanian to Early Permian interval, and were approximately contemporaneous with the intrusion of the underlying granites. In eastern Devon, sequences of Late Permian age lie above the deeply weathered surface of the volcanics, suggesting a substantial hiatus between the two. (Warrington and Scrivener, 1988).

Both seismic and aeromagnetic data suggest extensive development of lavas at the base of the Permo-Triassic sequence in the Melville Basin. Well data show that the top of the lava flows corresponds to a seismic reflector that can be mapped across much of the basin. The largest area is estimated to measure some 55 by 35 km, and contains up to 3000 m of lavas (BGS Little Sole Bank Solid Geology sheet) which accumulated in the western part of the basin to the south of the axis of major Triassic deposition (Chapman, 1988). This separation of the volcanic and later Triassic sediment depocentres suggests that the lava outpouring was not directly related to the extensional tectonics which led to the development of the Mesozoic basin.

Two wells in the Melville Basin proved volcanic sequences which are undated, although spatial relationships suggest that they are contemporaneous with the Exeter Volcanic Series. Well 74/1-1 terminated in 568 m of greenish grey to red, weathered, crystalline to microcrystalline tuff with chlorite inclusions, calcite veins and some reddish brown, silt-sized matrix. Rare sidewall cores recovered samples of pale green to grey, fine-grained, crystalline trachyte which may represent lava flows or breccias.

A similar sequence was penetrated in well 73/12-1A which recovered 295 m of weathered lava and tuff with interbedded, locally derived sandstone, breccia and conglomerate. The terminal core is a highly altered trachyandesite containing feldspar laths enclosing microphenocrysts altered to clay minerals and iron oxides. One of the lava flows in the core has an aphyric top but is microphyric and sparsely vesicular in the lowest 50 cm. The unit is cut by fractures filled with chlorite, calcite and minor quartz, and the vesicles are filled with calcite.

These trachyandesites are chemically different from the Exeter Volcanic Series, which are basic in character. Their trace elements show gross similarities with the contemporaneous lavas in south-west England, although a number of features, such as the La:Ta ratio, indicate derivation from a different mantle source.

Magnetic surveys reveal marked east-north-east-trending lineations (Figure 21) parallel to the axis of the Western Approaches Trough that were first considered to be the result of topographic variations in the Palaeozoic floor of the trough (Hill and Vine, 1965). Avedik (1975) and Lefort and Segoufin (1978) suggested that they reflect structural trends in the basement, but recent examination of data from the Melville Basin suggests that the anomalies are caused by Permian volcanics.

Pinet et al. (1987) suggest that some of the deeper reflectors (at 2.8 s TWTT) in the Permo-Triassic section of the Plymouth Bay Basin may be generated by volcanic horizons. A weaker line of anomalies in the St Mary's Basin runs parallel to the south-south-eastern edge of the Cornubian Platform and may be a function of weathered or thinner lavas, but could also be caused by ophiolites in the basement similar to those exposed on the Lizard. It is likely that all the magnetic anomalies in the Western Approaches Trough are related to Early Permian volcanic rocks, but it is not clear why they should form anomalies parallel to the long axis of the trough.

No dyke swarm has been recognised offshore which could have fed the suite of Permian lavas. However, a gravity anomaly at 49°33′N 6°58′W on the south-eastern flank of the Cornubian Batholith has been modelled as a steep-sided, dense body, termed the Madura body (Edwards, 1984), that may be a basic intrusive centre of Early Permian age.

5 Post-Carboniferous structural development

The collision between the continents of Gondwana and Laurasia culminated in Late Carboniferous times with the Variscan orogeny which produced two sets of major crustal discontinuities in the report area; north-east-trending Variscan thrusts, and slightly later north-north-west-trending transform faults (Figure 4). The tectonic history of the area since Late Carboniferous–Early Permian time has been determined largely by renewed movement along these discontinuities.

The Variscan orogeny ceased during the Early Permian to leave a rugged, arid landscape with intermontane basins containing volcanic rocks. By Late Permian to Early Triassic time, crustal rifting led to the formation of fault-bounded basins in which very thick redbed sequences accumulated; this was followed during the Jurassic by more widespread deposition of marine sequences. By the Middle Jurassic, renewed crustal stress produced local uplift, followed by more extensive doming and erosion during Late Jurassic to earliest Cretaceous time. Simultaneously, crustal stresses related to the opening of the North Atlantic led to the formation of local depocentres in the southern basins of the Western Approaches Trough. By the Aptian, oceanic crust was being created in the newly formed ocean at the base of the Western Approaches continental margin. During this rifting phase, the extended crust under the present continental slope suffered very rapid subsidence which then slowed at an exponential rate during the Late Cretaceous and early Tertiary. Tectonism was renewed during the Palaeogene as a result of collision between Europe and Africa; these Alpine stresses produced local uplift during the Paleocene, and a subsequent series of inversion pulses that reached a climax during the late Eocene to Oligocene. These movements continued sporadically at a reduced scale into the Miocene and helped fashion the present topography of the region.

TECTONIC MECHANISMS

Sedimentary basins form when stresses stretch and thin the lithosphere which is made up of the crust and upper mantle. There are two main hypotheses for the formation of basins related to such extension; the pure shear model derived from McKenzie (1978), and the simple shear model of Wernicke (1981).

The pure shear model of McKenzie (1978) is developed around the premise that tectonic extensional stresses cause the lithosphere to stretch and thin in a geologically short period of time. This produces an initial, rapid, isostatically adjusted, fault-controlled subsidence in the upper crust followed by a much slower phase of thermal relaxation subsidence as the raised asthenosphere cools, contracts and sinks. The two phases of subsidence impart a characteristic 'steer's head' cross-section to the sedimentary basins with their deep, fault-controlled central portions and outward thinning flanks (Dewey, 1982; White and McKenzie, 1988).

In an alternative model proposed by Wernicke (1981), simple shear extension of the lithosphere induces movement along pre-existing major low-angled faults or thrusts. This allows a complex of sedimentary basins and horsts to

form in the upper crust, while extension is accommodated at depth by ductile flow in the mantle. Beach (1987) developed this model (Figure 23a) with specific reference to the region surrounding the report area; in his model, the southward-dipping Variscan Front (Figure 4) is the major thrust or detachment across the region that forms an undulating plane with flats and ramps that extend into the mantle. Extension of the crust above the detachment produces a variety of basinal structures that are related to its inclination at depth; basins develop above detachment ramps, and the flats in the detachment are overlain by stratigraphic axes or highs.

In the report area, sedimentary basins formed by crustal subsidence have been subjected to periodic uplift or inversion. True tectonic inversion is related to compression of the crust leading to a change in the 'structural polarity' of an area (Lake and Karner, 1987) so that the basinal areas transform into structural highs and the structural highs become depocentres. In the model developed by Beach (1987), inversion occurs above ramps in the major crust-cutting thrust, (Figure 23b) while areas overlying the flats remain at the same level or become relative depocentres. Thus sedimentary basins that developed above the ramps during tensional phases become inverted during compression.

TECTONIC HISTORY

Figure 24 depicts the tectonic history of the northern and southern parts of the Western Approaches Trough as deduced by Hillis (1988) from well and seismic data. The post-Variscan tectonic history of the region can be divided into four phases.

1. Initial basin formation which began during the Late Permian to Early Triassic and terminated at the end of the Jurassic.
2. A complex tectonic episode during the Late Jurassic to Early Cretaceous that is dominated by doming and regional uplift of the northern basins of the Western Approaches Trough and the formation of oceanic crust adjacent to the Western Approaches margin.
3. A more tranquil post-rifting phase of slow, uniform subsidence from the end of the Early Cretaceous to the late Paleocene.
4. Inversion from early Eocene until Miocene time, cumulatively termed the Alpine event.

The rifting and subsidence phase — Early Permian to Late Jurassic

During the Permian, a system of rifts started to fracture the newly formed supercontinent of Pangaea, and by Triassic time, extension of the crust along these lines of weakness led to the formation of sedimentary basins across southern Britain and its surrounds (Chadwick, 1985 and 1986; Hillis, 1988). The rifts formed along the reactivated Variscan thrusts and north-west-trending dextral strike-slip faults. The basins were part of an Arctic–North Atlantic rift system linked with the development of basins in the Bay of Biscay and Rockall Trough (Ziegler, 1987a).

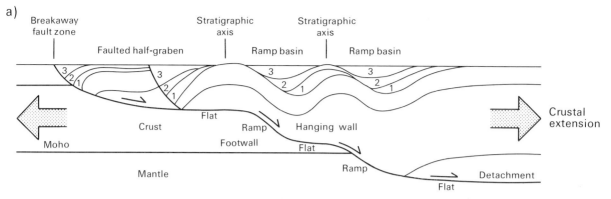

a)

Note that the figures relate to the stages in the development of the features

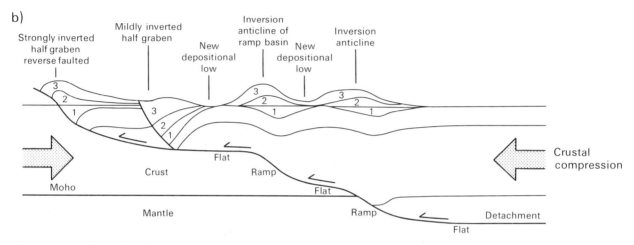

b)

Figure 23 Balanced sections showing schematically the deformation in the hanging wall above a detachment with, a) dip-slip movement during a phase of crustal extension, followed by b) reverse dip-slip movement during a phase of crustal compression. After Beach (1987).

The northern part of the Melville Basin remained a high throughout the Permian and did not receive any sediments until the Triassic subsidence phase (Figure 24a). Likewise, the Permian sediments in the Southwest Channel and Brittany basins are thin, and these basins also may have been end-Variscan topographic highs (Figure 24b). The Early Permian sediments in the southern part of the Melville Basin and the Plymouth Bay Basin were deposited in Variscan intermontane troughs with contemporaneous volcanics that were related to the final phases of emplacement of the granite batholiths. The loading of the Permian sediments onto the crust amplified the initial magnitude of the topographic low in the southern part of the Melville Basin to accommodate up to 4 km of sediments.

Chapman (1988) dates the initiation of rifting in the Melville Basin as Early Permian, but unequivocal evidence for crustal extension of this age is lacking in many basins in the North Atlantic region (Masson and Miles, 1986). In Devon the postorogenic volcanic rocks are of Early Permian age, but the accumulations of the main overlying redbed sequences did not commence until the Late Permian (Warrington and Scrivener, 1988 and in press). Discrete basins with considerable relief existed until Late Permian time, and these later coalesced to occupy the length of the Western Approaches Trough. As the rate of subsidence in the basins slowed with the peneplanation of the surrounding Variscan massifs, there may have been a period of

nondeposition prior to the onset of Triassic subsidence. The regional unconformities recognised on seismic profiles in Late Permian to Early Triassic sequences may be in part associated with this period of nondeposition.

During Early Triassic to earliest Late Triassic time, tensional stresses led to reactivation of the Variscan thrusts and transfer faults in the Melville Basin. This event signalled the onset of redbed deposition (Sherwood Sandstone Group) throughout the Western Approaches Trough, and caused a shift in the depositional axis from the southern to the northern part of the Melville Basin. The Sherwood Sandstone Group rests with minor unconformity on thick Permian sediments in the southern Melville Basin, and directly upon pre-Permian basement in the northern part of the basin. Rapid fault-controlled subsidence continued during the deposition of the overlying Mercia Mudstone Group, and died out towards the end of Triassic time. The onset of the thermal subsidence phase, combined with a eustatic rise in sea level, led to marine transgression over the peneplaned Late Triassic landscape. Subsidence continued into the Early Jurassic when the sediments covered a much larger area than is indicated by their present distribution. Over 1000 m of Jurassic sediments are preserved in the basin and their original thickness may have exceeded 2000 m. This widening of the basin during later stages of development is typical of the classic 'steer's head' cross-section described by Dewey (1982).

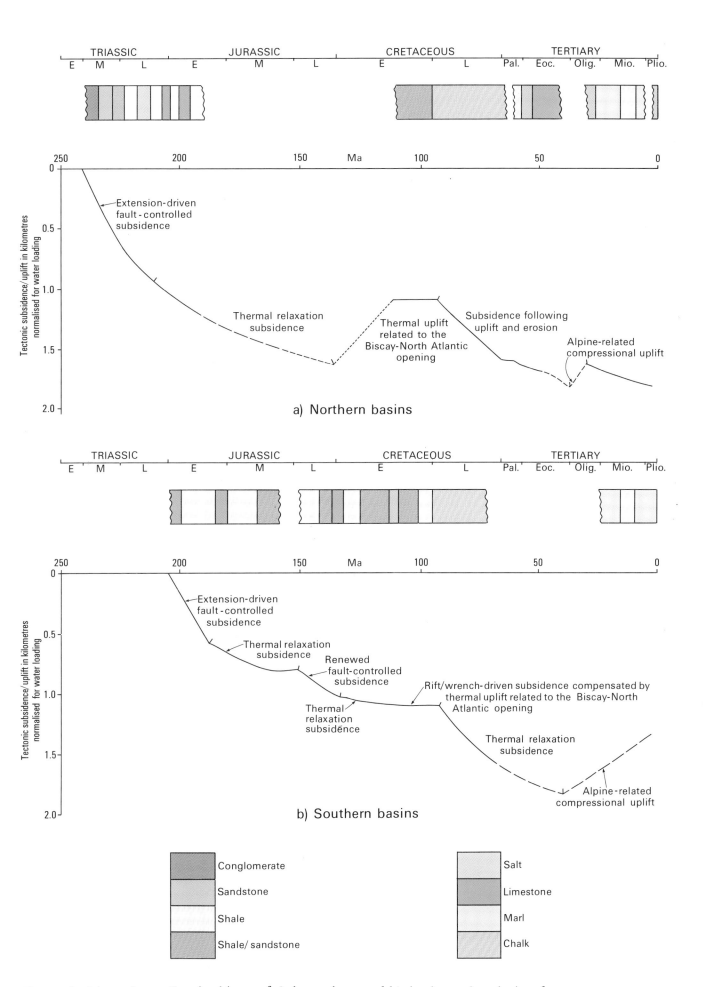

Figure 24 Schematic post-Permian history of a) the northern, and b) the the southern basins of the Western Approaches Trough. Modified from Hillis (1988).

The Plymouth Bay Basin is almost circular in plan and has a particularly thick Permo-Triassic sequence (>9 km) that shallows to the south against the Ouessant–Alderney fault zone (Figure 25). The basin overlies a southerly dipping crustal detachment zone related by Pinet et al. (1987) to an easterly extension of the Lizard Thrust. Major faulting and block-tilting is absent, and the basin infilled a gradually subsiding crustal sag. The continuity of the Variscan thrust underlying the basin demonstrates that the lower crust did not undergo excessive horizontal extension during basin formation, which implies that the form and thickness of the basin 'cannot be related easily to any rifting process' (Pinet et al., 1987, p.27).

The Ouessant–Alderney fault zone, the Principal Displacement Zone of Hillis (1988), and its south-westerly extension is a zone of major tectonic disturbance that may be a reactivated Cadomian or Caledonian structure (Figure 4). Lefort and Segoufin (1978) show a series of ophiolites of Palaeozoic age aligned along the fault zone. The cross-sections of Ziegler (1987b) show the Permo-Triassic sequences in the Western Approaches Trough thinning abruptly to the south across this fault zone. Significant strike-slip movement occurred along the fault in Late Jurassic and mid-Tertiary time, and it was a focus of a modern earthquake (Mourant, 1931). The fault zone forms the southern margin to the Southwest Channel Basin and, west of Ushant, defines the northern bounding fault to the Brittany Basin (Ziegler, 1987b).

Triassic sediments are thin or absent in the Southwest Channel and Brittany basins because the tensional stresses which ended by the Late Triassic in the northern part of the trough were intitiated in these southern basins at the beginning of Jurassic time. In the Brittany Basin, rapid, fault-controlled subsidence persisted until the Pliensbachian, resulting in a thick Lias sequence of similar facies to that of the same age in the gently sagging Melville Basin. The ensuing thermal subsidence continued in this basin until Bathonian to Callovian time with the deposition of thick calcareous mudstones. A regression in the basin at the end of the Middle Jurassic is not associated with significant deformation or erosion, and may be due to a combination of low subsidence rates and a eustatic fall in sea level. The Early to Middle Jurassic subsidence phase is not so well developed in the Southwest Channel Basin where rapid subsidence followed a Middle to Late Jurassic period of nondeposition. The onset of tectonic instability in these basins in Callovian times (Ziegler, 1987b) was approximately contemporaneous with the intrusion of basalt sills in the Fastnet Basin (Caston et al., 1981).

The South Celtic Sea Basin, which extends eastwards into the Bristol Channel Basin, also formed along reactivated Variscan thrusts during the Permo-Triassic rifting. The basin contains up to 3.3 km of Permian to Jurassic strata arranged in a series of synclinal, faulted grabens; seismic sections show a series of east-north-east-orientated normal faults delimiting the southern margin of the basin (Van Hoorn, 1987). Gardiner and Sheridan (1981) equate this system of south-easterly hading faults with the reactivation of underlying faults that are related to the south-westward extension of the Variscan Cannington Thrust which runs along the southern side of the Bristol Channel.

The Middle Jurassic to Early Cretaceous events

Tectonic events across north-west Europe from the Middle Jurassic into the Early Cretaceous (Ziegler, 1982) were the result of lithospheric stresses related to the opening of the North Atlantic. Within the report area, the events involved at least three episodes; Middle Jurassic uplift of limited extent, major regional uplift towards the end of Jurassic time, and localised rifting associated with strike-slip movement during the Early Cretaceous. Due to erosion associated with this regional uplift, Jurassic and Lower Cretaceous sediments are largely absent from the northern basins of the Western Approaches Trough, and evidence of these events is drawn mainly from the sequences preserved in the surrounding sedimentary basins. The uplift appears to have a symmetry centred on the Cornubian Ridge; the basins immediately to the north and south of the ridge were subject to uplift during the Late Jurassic to Early Cretaceous, but no significant unconformity of this age can be traced in the North Celtic Sea, Brittany and Southwest Channel basins, which are farther away from the uplift axis. The mechanism that caused the uplift may have been focused in the Cornubian Ridge by the low density material within its batholiths (Hillis, 1988).

A stratigraphic hiatus is recognised in the Middle and Upper Jurassic sediments of the Celtic Sea basins. In the South Celtic Sea Basin south of Pembrokeshire, it separates lower Callovian from Kimmeridgian and Portlandian sediments (Kamerling, 1979), and a similar break is recorded by Millson (1987) in the North Celtic Sea Basin. The limited erosion associated with the disconformity implies broad, gentle, regional uplift of limited magnitude.

The Late Jurassic to Early Cretaceous was a time of major uplift, when up to 2 km of Permian to Jurassic sediments were eroded from the northern basins of the Western Approaches Trough. The uplift was contemporaneous with the initiation of rifting on the continental margin, though its magnitude and extent are not directly related. Simultaneously, up to 2.5 km of sediments accumulated in the southern basin of the Western Approaches Trough (Hillis, 1988). Profiles across the northern part of the Western Approaches Trough (Figures 25 to 29) show the degree of downcutting increasing to the south towards the Ouessant–Alderney fault zone. Local subsidence involving renewed reactivation of the former Variscan thrusts and transfer faults also occurred, while salt withdrawal in the Melville Basin served to preserve isolated Lias outliers. The faulted northern boundary of the Melville Basin (Figure 26a and 27) formed at this time.

The rapid accumulation of sediments in the southern basins of the Western Approaches Trough is related to sinistral strike-slip movement along the Ouessant–Alderney fault zone. On SWAT line 8 there is no major fault between the Southwest Channel and Plymouth Bay basins, for here the fault zone forms the southern margin of the Southwest Channel Basin, and during Late Jurassic to Early Cretaceous time had a downthrow to the north. Farther west on SWAT line 7 (Figure 29b), the fault zone separates the Brittany and St Mary's basins, and shows a contemporary downthrow to the south. Towards the shelf edge, the polarity of the fault reverses again to downthrow to the north (Hillis, 1988). Strike-slip movement along this fault, with its curvilinear trace, generated tensional zones in the crust which became the foci for rapid subsidence. The extensional nature of faulting in the basins at this time suggests that motion along the fault zone was not purely strike-slip, and that some component of rifting was involved (Hillis, 1988). In the southern basins of the Western Approaches Trough, the magnitude of the local subsidence was much greater than that of the regional uplift, and restricted rapid deposition took place in a region which was undergoing broad uplift.

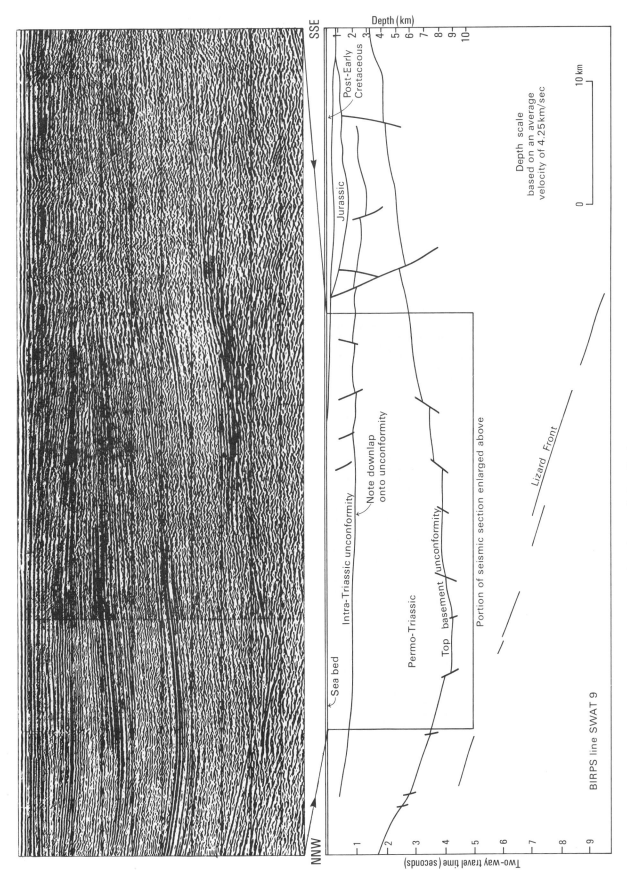

Figure 25 Seismic section and interpretation across the Plymouth Bay Basin. For location see Figure 6.

33

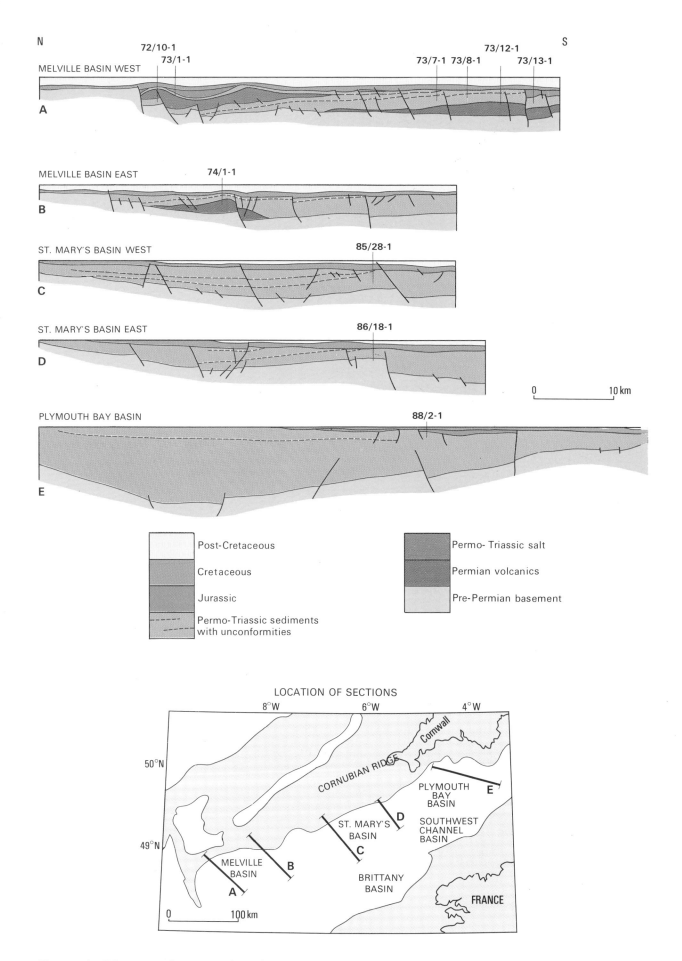

Figure 26 Diagrammatic cross-sections through the northern part of the Western Approaches Trough, showing the structural positions of wells.

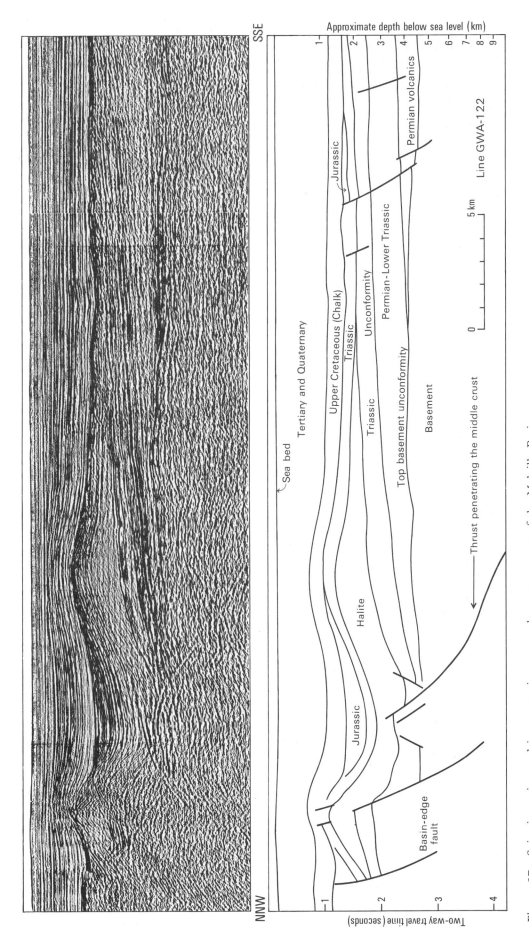

Figure 27 Seismic section and interpretation across the western part of the Melville Basin. For location see Figure 6.

35

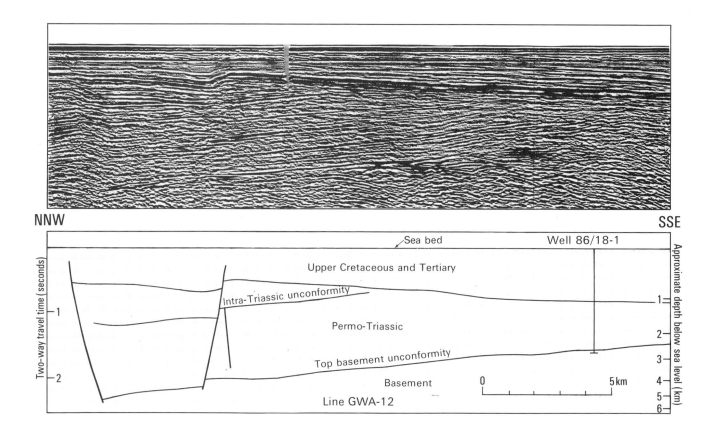

NNW   SSE

Figure 28   Seismic section and interpretation across the St Mary's Basin.
For location see Figure 6.

The opening of the North Atlantic

The Late Jurassic to Early Cretaceous tectonic events on the continental shelf coincided with rifting of the regional continental margin prior to the formation during the early Aptian of oceanic crust in the proto-North Atlantic (Montadert et al., 1979). The onset of sea-floor spreading in this newly formed ocean moved northward and started slightly later, during the late Albian, to the west of Goban Spur (de Graciansky and Poag, 1985).

In both the Aquitaine and Brittany basins, the onset of tensional stresses associated with events in the proto-North Atlantic area occurred in the Late Jurassic (Oxfordian), and was followed in the Early Cretaceous by the development in these basins of major half-grabens. The start of the rifting episode at the Western Approaches margin may have been contemporaneous with these events. Rifting reactivated the pre-existing basement faults along trends similar to those cutting the floor of the Melville Basin, and the present margin consists of a series of oceanward-tilted blocks bounded by listric faults and overlain by half-grabens. The trend of the fault-blocks follows the strike of the margin, which is orientated about 110° adjacent to the Meriadzek Terrace, and changes to 150° across the Goban Spur margin. The Shelf Edge Basin (Figures 4 and 30) is parallel to the fault pattern on the margin and contains early Mesozoic strata, but its bounding faults were not reactivated by the stresses which broke up the adjoining oceanward part of the margin.

Movement on the faults and rotation of the blocks stopped in the Aptian, at about the same time as sea-floor spreading began in the newly formed ocean basin farther west. During the Aptian, the outermost part of the margin subsided very rapidly to water depths of 1500 to 2000 m, and a narrow basin fronted the Western Approaches Trough. This faulting followed by rapid subsidence

equates with the initial rifting phase of basin development in the McKenzie (1978) model when the crust suffers rapid stretching. The upper 8 km of crust at the margin was stretched by a factor of ×3 during its brittle break-up into fault-blocks. The blocks rotated along listric fault planes which flattened out into the lower crust. This ductile lower crust was stretched and reduced in thickness from between 15 to 24 km away from the rifted zone to some 3 km under the outer margin, and zero at the ocean–continent crust boundary (Montadert et al., 1979).

Rifting took place in a marine environment without substantial doming of the adjacent unstretched proto-slope, although lateral conduction of heat into the litho-sphere under the present outer shelf may have produced a low outer shelf shoulder which persisted into the Late Cretaceous (Hillis, 1988).

The overall subsidence of the rifted margin was a result of isostatic subsidence related to the initial rifting, followed by thermal relaxation subsidence; subsidence decreased landward from a maximum at the ocean–continent boundary which lies some 200 km south-west of the present shelf edge. The total subsidence since rifting has been estimated from the change in the level of the Aptian marine erosion surface. When corrected for the loading effect of the sediment overburden, the outer margin has subsided by 4 km at the ocean–continent boundary but only by some 500 to 1000 m at the present shelf edge (Montadert et al., 1979).

The post-rifting phase—late Aptian to late Paleocene

The region was tectonically almost quiescent during this interval although the broad regional subsidence that continued through the Late Cretaceous, coupled with a high sea level, led to the accumulation of up to about 500 m of mostly chalk sediment across the Western Approaches

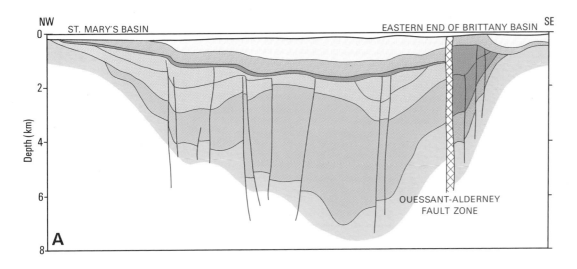

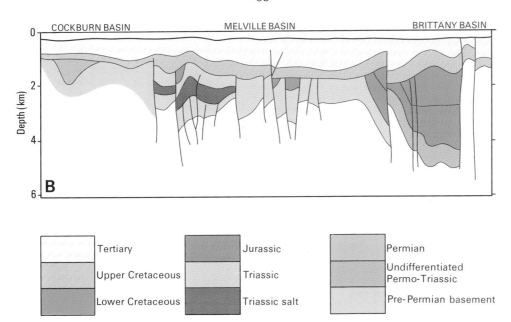

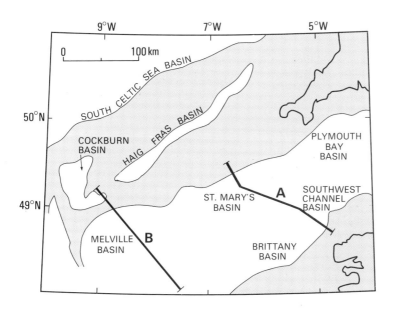

Figure 29 Diagrammatic sections across the Western Approaches Trough.
After Hillis (1988).

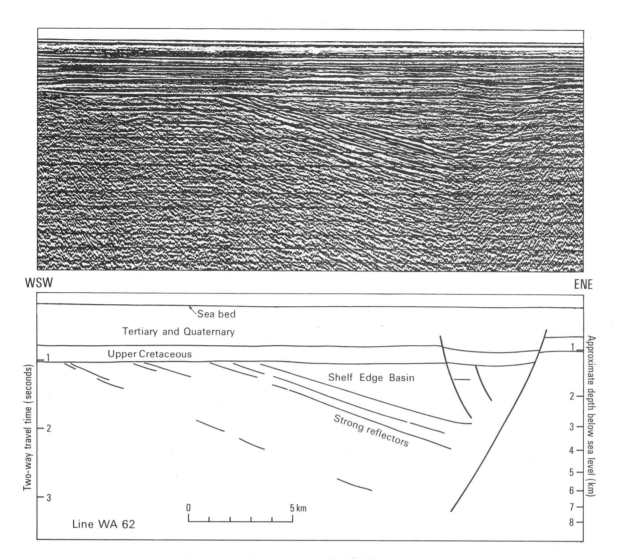

Figure 30 Seismic section and interpretation across the Shelf Edge Basin. For location see Figure 6.

In the figure:

WSW ... ENE

Sea bed
Tertiary and Quaternary
Upper Cretaceous
Shelf Edge Basin
Strong reflectors
Line WA 62

Two-way travel time (seconds)

0 ... 5 km

Approximate depth below sea level (km)

Trough. Subsidence of the northern basins of the Western Approaches Trough and the Cornubian Massif was due to cooling of the lithosphere following thermally driven uplift during the Late Jurassic. The subsidence in the southern basins of the Western Approaches Trough was enhanced by thermal relaxation following the Early Cretaceous lithospheric extension.

Thickness variations in the Upper Cretaceous Chalk across the area show that the basinal areas subsided faster than the flanking basement highs, and that the present gentle dip of the unit from east to west was not contemporaneous with deposition but a function of later Tertiary tilting. In the South Celtic Sea Basin, contemporaneous salt movement led to the accumulation of a locally enhanced thickness of Chalk.

In the Western Approaches Trough, early Alpine plate convergence combined with eustatic sea-level changes resulted in several minor Paleocene hiatuses, but these did not become regionally significant until the Eocene. The Paleocene disconformity across the Western Approaches Trough may be related to a eustatic fall in sea level rather than a tectonic event, although tectonism of this age is recorded in the Hampshire Basin, and the Fastnet Basin suffered substantial uplift during post-Maastrichtian to pre-middle Eocene time (Robinson et al., 1981).

The early Eocene emplacement of the Lundy Granite at Lundy Island (Figure 1) and its associated dyke swarm on the margin of the Bristol Channel Basin was the southernmost manifestation of the activity related to the Hebridean igneous province (Curry et al., 1978). Although the igneous plug affecting the top of the Chalk in the Fastnet Basin may be related to this activity (Caston et al., 1981), it is likely to be a younger Tertiary intrusion.

Alpine events — Eocene to Miocene

General considerations

By the early Palaeogene, subsidence at the outer shelf due to the Early Cretaceous rifting of the margin had become minimal, and the region lay to the south of the vulcanicity associated with the Hebridean igneous province. Southern Britain lay between two plate boundaries; the extensional boundary in mid-Atlantic, and the collision boundary that ran through the Mediterranean between the Eurasian and African plates. The tectonic events in the report area at this time were the result of transmitted stresses developed at these boundaries, although events at the continent/continent boundary in the Mediterranean which produced the Alpine mountain chain were the more important. The absence of synchroneity in fault movement and uplift between the various basins in the report area is a feature of the Alpine events, a pattern that is made difficult to unravel by the limited geographic and stratigraphic extent of the units associated with the deformational stages.

The collision between the Eurasian and African plates resulted in the formation of orogenic mountain belts and the radiation of deformation into the Eurasia continental hinterlands. Three separate orogenies are recognised in the Mediterranean region after the early Eocene: during the middle Eocene (about 45 Ma), during the middle Miocene (about 12 Ma), and during the late Miocene (about 6 Ma) (Muir Wood, 1989).

Stresses were transmitted through the continental hinterland with the crust acting as a stress guide, and relative horizontal movement between adjacent parts of the crust reactivated existing strike-slip and normal faults. Normal faults within basins may have been changed by compressional stresses into reverse faults that accommodated the necessary crustal shortening, and this caused uplift or inversion of the basins. The model of structures produced by crustal compression shown in Figure 23 (Beach, 1987) utilises a basal detachment thrust for transmitting the crustal movement; though no such structure has been identified from the seismic profiles across the area, the principle for tectonic inversion is valid, with movement taking place by the reactivation and polarity reversal of movement along several faults.

Continent/continent collision across southern France during the middle Eocene, led to the underthrusting of the Bay of Biscay oceanic crust beneath the north Iberia continental margin. The effects of this movement continued into the late Eocene along the Western Approaches Margin where oceanic crust was thrust under the continental margin at a transcurrent fault system to the west of the base of the Trevelyan Escarpment (Figure 13) (Masson and Parson, 1983). Simultaneously, to the east, some Mesozoic normal east–west faults in the Portland–Wight, Dorset and North Celtic Sea basins were reversed. This east–west inversion axis in the central English Channel passed south-westwards into renewed movement along the sinistral strike-slip Ouessant–Alderney fault zone. The 2 to 5 km crustal shortening implied by this inversion was accommodated along north-west-trending strike-slip faults such as the Sticklepath–Lustleigh Fault. Movement along this fault transferred a few kilometres of displacement into the eastern end of the Celtic Sea basins which suffered inversion of between 1 and 3 km during the middle Eocene (Muir Wood, 1989).

Though Muir Wood (1989) recognises no continent/continent collision along the Mediterranean boundary during late Eocene to early Miocene time, there is evidence of continued tectonic activity across southern Britain. A renewed phase of movement in the middle to late Oligocene along the Sticklepath–Lustleigh Fault led to enhanced subsidence in the Bovey Basin, and there was further movement along the Ouessant–Alderney fault zone, while a number of Oligocene basins developed near to major fault lines along the coast of western Britain (Wilkinson et al., 1980). Compressional deformation of the Brittany Basin, synchronous with movement along the Ouessant–Alderney fault zone, induced upwarping of a major anticlinorium that 'had a structural relief of some 3000 m' (Ziegler, 1987b, p.345), and sinistral movement may have occurred along the faults bounding the South Celtic Sea Basin. In the absense of synchronous tectonic activity along the Mediterranean boundary at this time, Muir Wood (1989) relates these movements to changes in plate motion in mid-Atlantic, or to a residual effect from lithospheric weakness associated with the early Palaeogene Hebridean igneous activity.

Postdepositional deformation of the Oligocene basins around southern Britain points to a general uplift of mainland Britain to produce the present south-easterly tilt across southern and eastern England. Compressional deformation of early Miocene sediments along parts of the Ouessant–Alderney fault zone and the shallowing of the shelf at this time point to a correlation between these movements and the middle Miocene orogeny in southern Iberia.

Italy collided with central Europe in the late Miocene to cause uplift of about 100 m in the Paris Basin and create a region of broad compressional deformation through Britain, Ireland, the English Channel and northern France. Uplift was greatest across western Britain, which suggests that some deformation transmitted from the mid-Atlantic spreading ridge was also involved.

The Western Approaches Trough and South Celtic Sea Basin

Paleocene tectonic movements across the Western Approaches Trough gently uplifted the Upper Cretaceous Chalk by a few hundred metres. This uplift combined with eustatic sea-level changes to produce a widespread, uniform, regional unconformity. In contrast, the later Alpine events were an order of magnitude greater and not as uniformly distributed.

The South Celtic Sea Basin was the first part of the report area to suffer significant Tertiary inversion. The late Eocene to early Oligocene sand and lignite resting on Upper Cretaceous Chalk across the southern part of this basin dates the uplift of the Celtic Sea basins as Paleocene to middle Eocene. This uplift was probably contemporaneous with the post-Maastrichtian to pre-middle Eocene inversion of the Fastnet Basin that was associated with compression during lateral movements along north-west-trending strike-slip faults (Robinson et al., 1981). The sand in the post-inversion, late Eocene sediments of the South Celtic Sea Basin must have come from the erosion of either a massif area or an Early Cretaceous Wealden section, for the sequences immediately underlying it are either calcareous or fine-grained clastic sediments. The incorporation of late Eocene to early Oligocene sediments into halokinetic structures in the South Celtic Sea Basin implies that fault movement in the basin continued during this period.

The sequences in the northern basin of the Western Approaches Trough record only a minor change in sedimentation in the middle Eocene, and continue with little lithological change into the late Eocene to terminate at the overlying unconformity. The tectonic inversion of these basins occurred between late Eocene and mid-Oligocene time. A thick Palaeogene sequence is preserved in the northern basins of the Western Approaches Trough, but across the Brittany Basin, where the magnitude of the uplift was greater, the Tertiary, and in places most of the Upper Cretaceous strata, have been removed (Ziegler, 1987b). Over 2 km of movement, downthrowing to the north, took place locally along the south-westward extension of the Ouessant–Alderney fault zone during this period. Only minor reverse faults or zones of intense Tertiary compressional deformation have been recognised from the northern basins of the Western Approaches Trough (Hall, 1986). Hillis (1988) explains this absence of deformation as due to the crust underlying these northern basins being sufficiently strong to transmit compressive stresses witiout itself deforming. However, there was movement along the Sticklepath–Lustleigh Fault in eastern Devon that extends northwards offshore into the

Bristol Channel where the Stanley Basin sediments accumulated (Fletcher, 1975).

Hillis (1988) estimated the magnitude of Tertiary uplift across the Western Approaches Trough by examining the porosity of the Upper Cretaceous Chalk. The results of these calculations (Figure 31), which assume all the uplift to be associated with the late Eocene to middle Oligocene event and none with any Paleocene uplift, show that a sequence between 400 and 800 m thick was eroded off the Melville Basin during this time. The magnitude of erosion increased north-eastwards into the English Channel where a sequence estimated to be between 800 and 1300 m thick was removed. Values at two sites in the Brittany Basin indicate the removal of between 1000 and 1400 m of sediment, and seismic profiles show that this value increases northwards towards the Ouessant–Alderney fault zone (Ziegler, 1987b). The Hillis (1988) calculations imply that, in the Melville Basin, a middle Eocene to mid-Oligocene sequence some 400 to 800 m thick was removed. Consideration of the time span of the hiatus (about 10 to 15 Ma), and the regional Eocene thickness, would suggest that these values are excessive. This may be in part a function of the anomalous position near salt swells of many data points, and possible porosity increases during uplift.

Hillis (1988) considered that the uplift extended southwestwards to the continental slope, though Ziegler (1987b, p.345) described it as fading out 'towards the Armorican shelf margin'. This uplift introduced a relative tilt of between 400 and 500 m west-south-westward in the Western Approaches Trough that is now evident from the contours of the basal Tertiary horizon. The contours of the base lower Miocene Jones Formation show a similar but lesser inclination related to the late Miocene uplift of mainland Britain and subsidence of the outer continental slope. This uplift may have continued into the early Pleistocene, for channels at the base of the upper Little Sole Formation are oblique to the present dip of the shelf and some deepen eastwards (Bouysse et al., 1976).

Transfer faults

During regional compression, the crust may be divided into blocks by transfer faults along which differential horizontal movement takes place. Some of the north-west-trending faults which formed during the Variscan orogeny were reactivated during both the Mesozoic extensional phase and the Alpine compressional phase. The best known of these is the Sticklepath–Lustleigh Fault in eastern Devon, which is composed of a series of left-stepping, *en-échelon* faults (Holloway and Chadwick, 1986). The fault zone forms a dextral offset of about 1.3 km to the eastern margin of the Dartmoor granite, and a slightly greater offset to the Crediton Trough. The Bovey Basin is the largest of a series of pull-apart basins formed along this fault zone during Eocene to Miocene time. For such basins to form on left-stepping faults, movement along the fault zone must be sinistral. Holloway and Chadwick (1986) therefore proposed that the early movement on the fault during Late Carboniferous to Early Permian time was dextral, and up to 6 km greater than the present 1.3 km dextral offset. During the early Tertiary, sinistral movement reduced this dextral offset to its present magnitude, though some minor dextral movement may have taken place after the deposition of the Bovey Formation.

Other transfer faults with the same orientation are shown crossing the region (Figure 4); their location is not well defined and no pull-apart basins of Tertiary age are

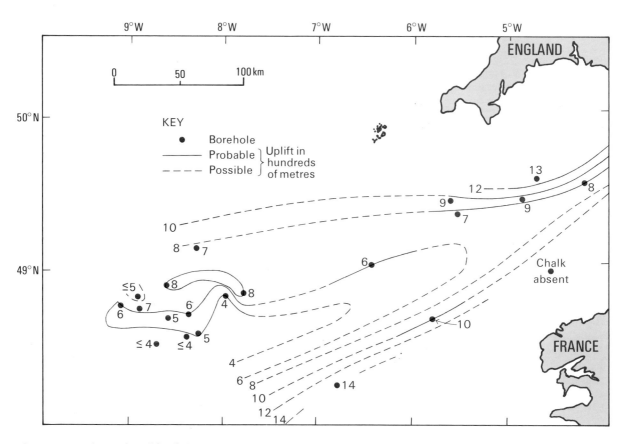

Figure 31 Estimated uplift of the Western Approaches Trough during the middle Tertiary tectonic inversion. After Hillis (1988).

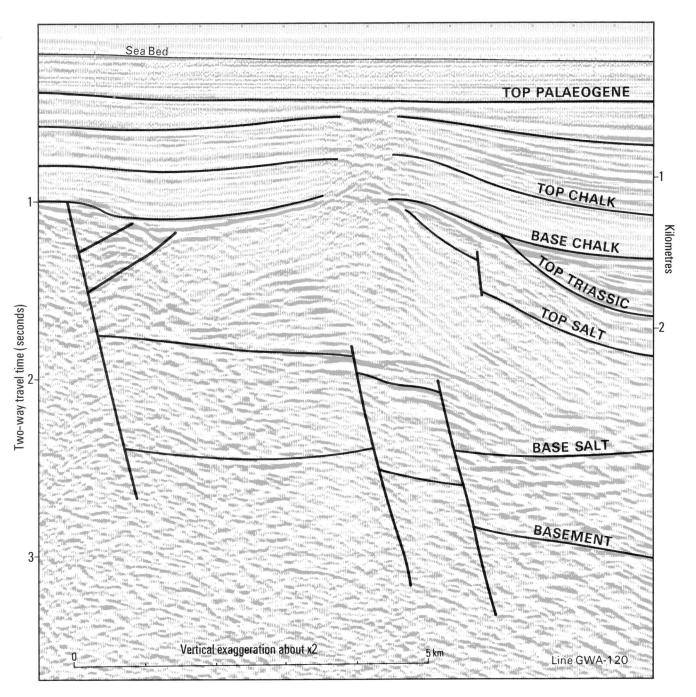

Two-way travel time (seconds)

Sea Bed

TOP PALAEOGENE

TOP CHALK

BASE CHALK

TOP TRIASSIC

TOP SALT

BASE SALT

BASEMENT

Kilometres

Vertical exaggeration about x2

0   5 km

Line GWA-120

Figure 32 Seismic section across a salt swell in the Melville Basin. For location see Figure 6.

known to be associated with them. The fault zone shown between the Isles of Scilly and the mainland is identified only from the displacement of the gravity anomaly produced by the Cornubian Batholith. The aeromagnetic map indicates a similar fault zone crossing the Melville Basin that is also recognised on seismic profiles (Hall, 1986; Hillis, 1988).

The development of the present topography

The granite batholiths of Cornubia formed upstanding masses of uncertain relief during the Cretaceous, and Freshney et al. (1982) suggest that the landmass attained its present form during the Eocene. Broad, episodic uplift and very localised subsidence has taken place since the Eocene, and may have kept the present land surface largely uncovered since the Oligocene (Walsh et al., 1987).

South-west England was probably uplifted during the late Eocene to early Oligocene inversion which affected the Western Approaches Trough. Because of the almost complete removal of Mesozoic and Tertiary sediments from the region, the magnitude of this uplift onshore cannot be assessed, though it may have been of the order of hundreds of metres (Figure 31). The uplifted land surface had been deeply weathered during the Eocene, when a uniformly warm climate prevailed across the region and erosion following uplift rapidly removed the regolith to reveal the present characteristic granite tors. The next phase of uplift occurred after the deposition of the early to middle Miocene sediments of the shelf; to the south respectively of the Bristol Channel and Ouessant–Alderney fault zones, the peninsulas of Devon/Cornwall and Brittany were uplifted in response to crustal compression that reactivated these reverse fault zones (Beach, 1987). This uplift raised the high planation surfaces across south-west England to their present elevation.

Halokinesis

Evaporite sequences, primarily of halite up to 2000 m thick, are found in the northern part of the Melville Basin and in the South Celtic Sea Basin. Halite is ductile under low external pressure, and lateral differences in pressure, as may occur across faults, can cause it to flow into swells synchronously with, or soon after, faulting.

In the northern part of the Melville Basin there are two major salt swells with adjoining withdrawal features. These are aligned approximately north-east to south-west, parallel to the main dip-slip faults within the basement (Hall, 1986). The continuity and uniformity of thickness of the Upper Cretaceous across the swells shows that the first major salt movements predated deposition of the Chalk and were probably related to the Late Jurassic to Early Cretaceous uplift of the basin. This episode of halokinesis and the later mid-Tertiary episode are both associated with periods of fault movement within the basin. The surface of the swells are planed off at the Early Cretaceous unconformity, and the halite subcrops locally beneath the Chalk. This unconformity was itself upraised during a second episode of salt movement in the Palaeogene. Contemporaneous uplift of the swells, coupled with associated subsidence and deposition in the surrounding areas during the early Tertiary, is shown on seismic profiles by the onlap of reflectors onto the flanks of the swells (Figure 32). This se-

cond period of movement, associated with late Eocene to early Oligocene regional uplift, produced enhanced erosion over the crests of the swells. During the mid-Tertiary, probably in the mid-Oligocene, movement largely stopped, and the later sediments were deposited unconformably and approximately horizontally over the halokinetic structures. Some seismic profiles suggest that very slight halokinetic movement has continued to affect sediments up to the sea bed.

Where groundwater comes into contact with halite, dissolution occurs and the halite and any overlying rocks may collapse. Figure 32 shows that flexure of the salt swell during the Tertiary was associated with dissolution of the halite and collapse of the central core of the structure. Such collapse is widely developed along the crest of the swell, and its precise form is dependent on the thickness of overburden. Where erosion has cut down close to the halite, zones showing dissolution appear as broad, confused bands on both seismic profiles and dipmeter logs.

The salt swells in the South Celtic Sea Basin also show two phases of movement. The first phase is assigned to the late Berriasian to pre-Aptian tectonic event when linear salt intrusions developed associated with faults and flexures in the basement. The second phase, which began in the mid-Tertiary, induced a salt pillow that has warped and fractured Upper Cretaceous, Tertiary and possibly Quaternary strata up to the sea bed (Kamerling, 1979). Additionally, the unusually thick 844 m of chalk recovered in well 93/2-1 is possibly a function of slow syndepositional salt movement during the Late Cretaceous.

6 Permo-Triassic

The orientation of the basins formed during the early Mesozoic and Permian in the report area cuts across the strike of the onshore Late Palaeozoic rocks, but parallels the Variscan thrusts which traverse the area (Ziegler, 1987b). Figure 33 shows the depth to the base of the Permo-Triassic sequence, which has been used to define the offshore Permian to Tertiary sedimentary basins (Figure 4). The contours pick out the major north-east-trending Western Approaches Trough, with a shallow saddle between Start Point and the Cotentin Peninsula separating it from the Portland–Wight Basin to the east. Within the trough there are a number of locally deeper centres such as the Plymouth Bay Basin where over 9 km of Permo-Triassic rocks accumulated. Post-Carboniferous sequences are thin or absent over the Cornubian Platform, except in the Haig Fras Basin. The South Celtic Sea Basin, which lies north of the Cornubian Platform, is parallel to the Western Approaches Trough and contains in excess of 1.5 km of Permo-Triassic strata (Van Hoorn, 1987).

The northward drift of Pangaea during the Carboniferous brought the area during the Permo-Triassic into latitudes with a more arid climate, and redbeds dominate the sequences. From their inception until Late Triassic time, the basins were above or temporarily only slightly below sea level. Thick Carnian to Norian halites record the first major influx of saline water into the basins, extending into the western part of the Western Approaches Trough and probably along the South Celtic Sea Basin into the Bristol Channel and Somerset. A major eustatic rise in sea level that started during the Norian (Haq et al., 1987) led to a marine transgression across the area and the deposition of marine Rhaetian and Jurassic claystones and limestones.

Cornford et al. (1987) estimate from vitrinite reflection measurements that the Carboniferous Bude and Crackington formations in north Cornwall have been buried to a depth of between 5.8 and 7.0 km, and it is probable that most of this overburden was removed during Permo-Triassic time. Indeed, Lake and Karner (1987) suggest that most of this erosion occurred during the Permian, when up to 10 km of sediment was removed from the highlands surrounding the Wessex Basin in southern England. Seismic sections show that erosion in the basinal areas had, prior to Permo-Triassic deposition, largely levelled any major relief associated with the Variscan orogeny. Local fault scarps were probably active but were only of minor importance. The most significant evidence for a major topographic feature within the Western Approaches Trough is in the Melville Basin where the redbeds onlap a volcanic pile. The troughwide continuity of the succession implies that an arid basin of gentle relief, traversed by fluvial and lacustrine systems, had developed across the region by the Early Triassic. The absence of coarser clastic sediments in the overlying Jurassic strata signifies that the adjacent basement massifs had been reduced to very low topographic features by the end of the Triassic, and may then have been inundated by the marine transgression.

Permo-Triassic sediments crop out at sea bed on the flanks of the major syncline occupying the western English Channel. To the south and west, an almost ubiquitous sheet of Cretaceous Chalk covers older strata (Figure 3), though Permo-Triassic rocks crop out as a discontinuous band along the northern flank of the Cornubian Platform and onshore in eastern Devon (Laming, 1982).

In broad stratigraphic terms, the Permo-Triassic sequences offshore are similar to those in southern Britain (Warrington et al., 1980); the extensive basal volcanic section (see Chapter 4) shows some chemical affinities (Edmonds et al., 1975) with the Permian volcanic rocks in Devon. Offshore, the volcanics pass up into breccias and conglomerates which are overlain by finer-grained redbeds of probable Permian or Early Triassic age that are equivalent to the Aylesbeare Group (Figure 5). The overlying sandstones and conglomerates are equivalent to, and informally equated with, the Sherwood Sandstone Group, and the upper part of the sequence is predominantly fine-grained, anhydritic claystone and marl with local halite that correlates with the Mercia Mudstone Group. Near the top of the Triassic, a shallow-marine influence is represented across the area by the claystone and limestone sequence of the Penarth Group.

The five cross-sections in Figure 26 summarise the pattern of post-Carboniferous stratigraphy in the northern part of the Western Approaches Trough, and show the relative location of wells quoted in the text. Success in dating the clastic redbed sequences has been limited, with most information in the youngest part of the succession that was deposited under shallow-marine influence. These dates, when based only on cuttings, should be used with care, for downhole contamination can result in anomalously younger ages.

WESTERN APPROACHES TROUGH

The contours on the base Permo-Triassic horizon show the northern part of the trough divided into three basins (Figure 33); the partially fault-bounded Melville Basin in the west, passing eastwards into the elongate St Mary's Basin that merges across a low col south-west of Cornwall with the almost circular Plymouth Bay Basin.

Melville Basin

The Melville Basin is a major depocentre underlying the outer continental shelf where the base of the Permo-Triassic sequence is at a maximum depth in excess of 7 km (Figure 33). The northern and western margins of the Permo-Triassic strata in the basin have been faulted against the Cornubian Platform and Little Sole Horst (Figures 4 and 26). At these faulted margins, the Permo-Triassic sequence is between 3 and 4 km thick, but thickens to the south before thinning again along the southern margin of the Brittany Basin (Ziegler, 1987b). In general, the youngest Permo-Triassic sediments are preserved only in the northern part of the basin (Figures 26 and 27), although local downfaulting in the south has preserved the top of the Triassic around well 73/13-1.

The oldest recovered sediments lying unconformably on the Early Permian volcanics are the thick, undated arenites, conglomerates and breccias, that include volcanic clasts in well 73/12-1A (Figure 34). This clastic sequence onlaps the volcanic pile to the south and downlaps onto

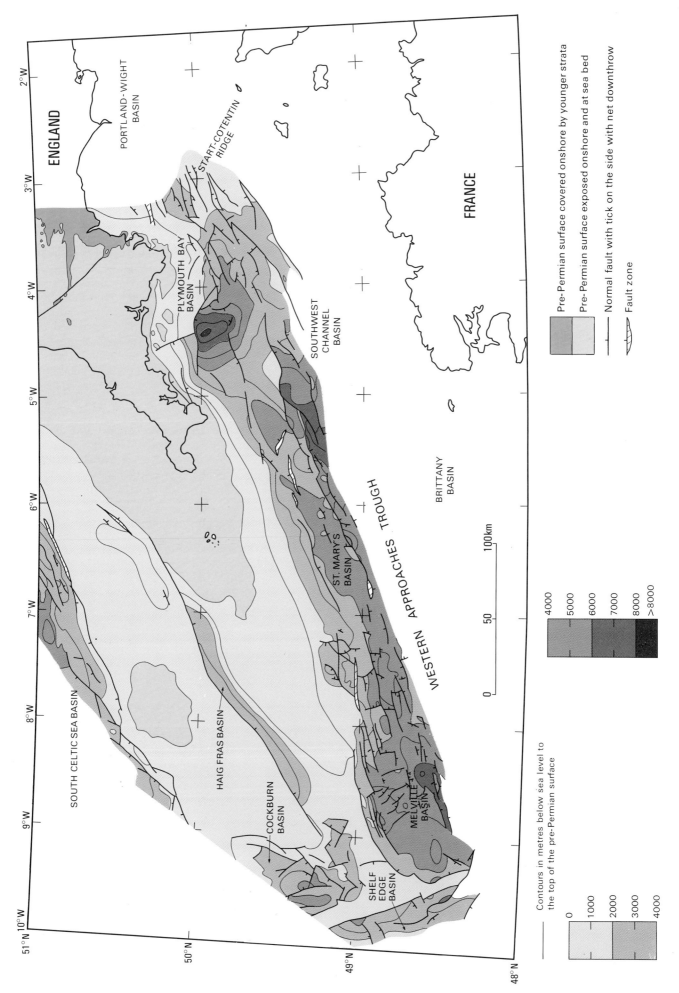

Figure 33 Depth to the pre-Permian surface. After N J P Smith (1985).

44

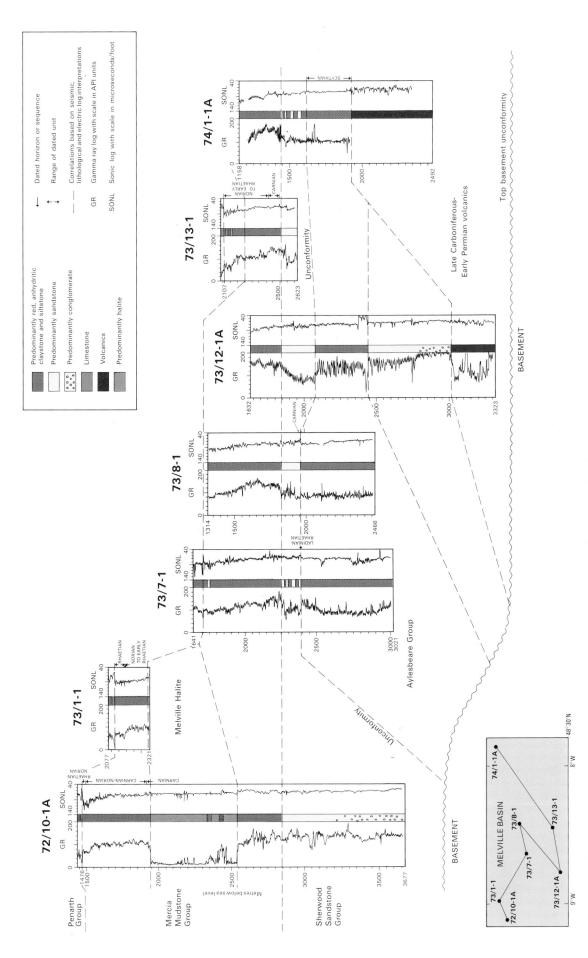

Figure 34 Simplified correlation diagram of Permo-Triassic sections from wells in the Melville Basin.

the basement to the north. The rocks fine upward into red, calcareous and anhydritic siltstones that are lithologically equivalent to the red mudstone and siltstone in the lowest part of wells 73/7-1 and 73/8-1, and those directly above the volcanics in well 74/1-1A. These sediments may be stratigraphically equivalent to the Late Permian to Early Triassic Aylesbeare Group onshore (Warrington et al., 1980). The basal units were probably laid down as major alluvial fans interspersed with braided-stream deposits; the sediments became finer as the landscape was reduced to a lowland environment that suffered short-lived, periodic marine incursions.

The 837 m-thick basal clastic unit in well 72/10-1A consists of reddish brown sandstone, breccia and conglomerate with haematite and calcite cements commonly developed. The basal core contains conglomeratic layers set in a fine-grained, argillaceous sandstone matrix. Bennet et al. (1985) and Fisher and Jeans (1982) tentatively suggest that this sequence is comparable with the Permian deposits of south-west England, but regional seismic correlation suggests that part or the whole of the unit may be equivalent to the Sherwood Sandstone Group, the clastic sandstone unit overlying the minor unconformity at the top of the Aylesbeare Group. This unconformity (Figures 26 and 34) is traceable across the basin and is considered to be of Late Permian to Early Triassic age.

The unconformity in other wells is overlain by a clastic unit made up of red arkose and quartz arenite, locally conglomeratic and containing thick fining-upward sequences; the conglomerate and sandstone sequences in well 73/14-1A are up to 25 m thick, and frosted grains occur in the sandstones. In well 73/8-1 Carnian palynomorphs were recovered from sandstone below siltstone and claystone that yielded a Carnian to Rhaetian palynoflora. These sandstones beneath the Mercia Mudstone Group compare with the Otter Sandstone Formation in Devon, which is of mid-Triassic (Anisian to Ladinian) age. The apparent younger age indicated offshore for these sandstones may be due to caving.

Above the sandstones is a sequence of greyish red, silty claystones which change upward to an olive-grey colour. Anhydrite, as nodules and in veins, and occasional interbedded dolomitic limestone, siltstone and sandstone occur within the claystones. This unit is equivalent to the Mercia Mudstone Group of Warrington et al. (1980). In well 72/10-1A it is 1364 m thick and Carnian to Norian in age (Bennet et al., 1985), and about half the unit consists of the Melville Halite. The non-saliferous part of the Mercia Mudstone Group in wells 72/10-1A, 73/7-1 and 73/13-1 is thicker in the northern part of the basin than in the south (Figures 26 and 34).

By the onset of deposition of the Melville Halite, the centre of subsidence lay within an east-north-east-trending trough in the northern half of the basin, where eventually up to 1200 m of evaporites accumulated (Figure 35). The sequence thins to the south where parallel, moderately strong seismic reflectors suggest a marginal evaporitic facies containing more anhydrite and carbonate (Hall, 1986). The Melville Halite (Figure 34) is at the same general stratigraphic level as that found in the South Celtic Sea Basin (well 93/6-1, Figure 36).

The Melville Halite has undergone halokinesis in two periods of movement (see p.41), and the resulting swells in overlying formations (Hall, 1986; Bennet et al., 1985) have formed the primary hydrocarbon targets in the area (Figures 26, 27 and 32). Two major salt swells have developed with an east-north-east orientation parallel to the fault forming the northern flank of the basin (Figure 35). Doming related to salt movement in the southern part of the basin led to exposure of the halite prior to the Cretaceous and a substantial volume may have dissolved away. The probable base of the halite zone occurs near the top of the Permo-Triassic section in well 73/7-1 where dipmeter results indicate a disrupted section 200 m thick that may be related to collapse after dissolution of halite.

The transition to marine sediments at the top of the Triassic is preserved in wells 72/10-1A, 73/1-1, 73/13-1 and in part in 73/14-1 (Figure 34). In well 72/10-1A, the

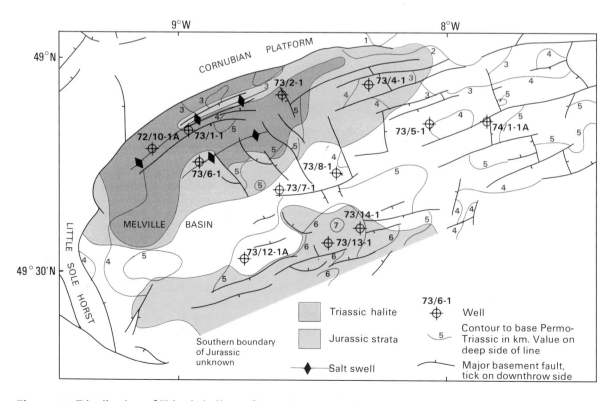

Figure 35 Distribution of Triassic halite and Jurassic strata in the Melville Basin.

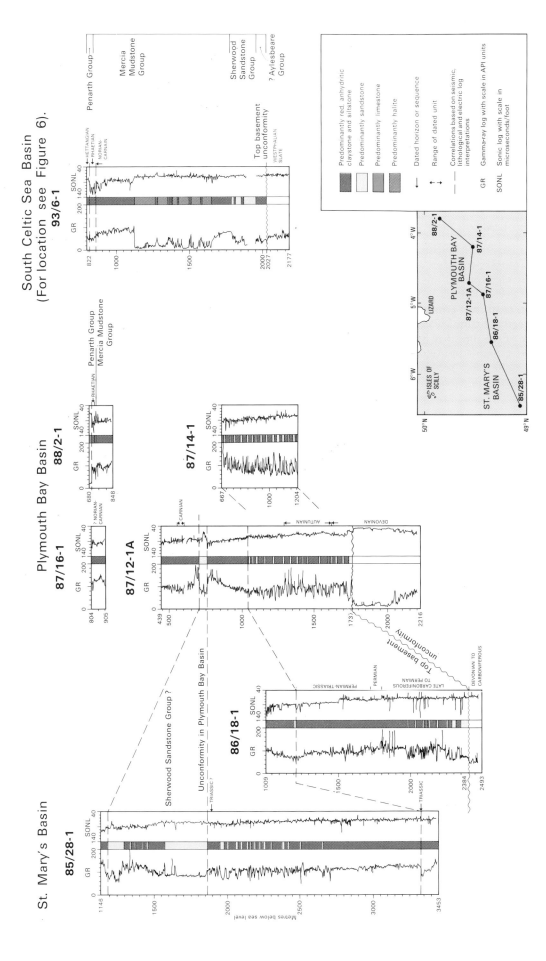

Figure 36 Simplified correlation diagram of Permo-Triassic sections in the St Mary's, Plymouth Bay and South Celtic Sea basins.

boundary between the Mercia Mudstone Group and the overlying Penarth Group is marked by the change from olive-grey claystone to a 23 m-thick, dark grey claystone containing thin beds of dolomitic limestone. This passes up into a 10 m-thick, pale grey to brownish grey, hard, blocky limestone which may equate with the 'White Lias' of southern England. Following Bennet et al. (1985), the base of the Lower Lias is placed at the base of the thick limestone, which is slightly lower than the Triassic–Jurassic boundary as defined by Warrington et al. (1980); see also Warrington (1983).

St Mary's and Plymouth Bay basins

Eastwards from the Melville Basin, the northern margin of the Western Approaches Trough becomes a normal contact, and the sediments generally dip to the south (Figure 26). However, the effects of post-Triassic to pre-Cretaceous tectonic uplift increase in intensity southwards, and in the southern part of the basin the Permo-Triassic generally thins to the south as the overlying Chalk and Tertiary units thicken (Figure 28). Seismic evidence indicates that up to 9 km of Permo-Triassic strata are preserved in the Plymouth Bay Basin, and about 4 to 6 km in the deepest parts of the St Mary's Basin.

The stratigraphy of the St Mary's Basin was tested in wells 85/28-1 and 86/18-1 (Figure 36). Both wells are sited on tilted fault-blocks formed during the pre-Cretaceous uplift. In well 86/18-1, the anhydritic shale with thin sandstones above the basal conglomerate is Late Carboniferous to Permian in age in its lower part, but Permo-Triassic in the upper section. Seismic correlations suggest that the base of the overlying interbedded red shale unit, with its thin basal sandstone, may be an unconformity which decreases in magnitude westwards to be barely traceable in 85/28-1. The base of a thick sandstone at 1858 m in well 85/28-1 may be equivalent to the base of the Sherwood Sandstone Group in well 74/1-1A, in which case the unconformity recorded in well 86/18-1 is at a stratigraphically lower level than that in the Melville Basin.

Between the St Mary's Basin and the Plymouth Bay Basin there is a slight shallowing of the basement (Avedik, 1975), and the Permo-Triassic sequence across this high was tested in well 87/12-1A (Figure 33). The 60 m thick sandstone below sediments of possible Carnian age may be lithologically equivalent to the Sherwood Sandstone Group. At the base of this sandstone is an angular unconformity which may correlate with that around the same stratigraphic position in the Melville Basin. On SWAT line 9, crossing the Plymouth Bay Basin, strata beneath this erosion surface are truncated and those above downlap on-to it (Figure 25).

The Permo-Triassic sediments onlap basement at the margins of the broadly circular Plymouth Bay Basin, which underwent contemporaneous downsagging and infill. Thinning of the sequences across the southern part of the basin is the result of intra-Triassic and Late Jurassic erosion. Wells 88/2-1, 87/14-1 and 87/16-1 were drilled on the southern and eastern flanks of the Plymouth Bay Basin; the log characteristics of the undated interbedded sandstone and siltstone in well 87/14-1 are similar to the Permian sequence in well 87/12-1A, a correlation which is supported by seismic evidence. Well 88/2-1, drilled into a small half-graben that lies between the eastern flank of the Plymouth Bay Basin and the Start–Cotentin Ridge (Evans et al., 1981), proved a conformable top to the Triassic, which includes a Rhaetian sequence similar to that in Dorset and the Melville Basin (Warrington, 1983).

Southwest Channel and Brittany basins

The thickness of Permo-Triassic sediments in these basins is generally much less than in the adjoining basins to the north. The basins contain a maximum of about 5 km of Permo-Triassic sediment, but in some areas, primarily on the southern flanks of the basins, they are thin or absent, and a thick Jurassic or younger sequence rests directly on or near basement (Ziegler, 1987b). In well Lennket-1, drilled on the southern flank of the Southwest Channel Basin, Lower Jurassic sandstone rests directly on metamorphosed monzonitic basement. To the south-west, in the centre of the Brittany Basin, well Brezell-1 penetrated a 219 m thick unit of red, feldspathic, micaceous, locally microconglomeratic sandstone of Permian age beneath an upper, 32 m thick, grey, fine- to medium-grained sandstone with argillaceous intercalations that is overlain by Hettangian claystone.

BASINS ON, AND NORTH OF, THE CORNUBIAN PLATFORM

The Haig Fras Basin is a shallow half-graben within the Cornubian Platform between the Haig Fras granite and south-west England. Strata in the graben dip to the north-west and extend south-westwards towards the northern margin of the Melville Basin (Figures 4 and 33). Seismic evidence suggests that up to 600 m of Permo-Triassic strata are preserved at the centre of the basin. Boreholes drilled across the southern part of the basin (BGS Haig Fras Solid Geology sheet) proved up to 24 m of undated red mudstone and sandstone under a variable thickness of Lower Cretaceous sand and clay.

In the north-east-trending, partially fault-bounded South Celtic Sea Basin, the base of the Permo-Triassic lies at a maximum depth of over 5 km (Figure 33), and the unit has a thickness in excess of 1500 m (Van Hoorn, 1987). Well 93/6-1 (Figure 36) tested a salt swell in the basin and proved a Permo-Triassic succession 1205 m thick that is lithologically similar to that in the northern part of the Melville Basin. At the base, unconformably overlying Westphalian slate, is a 76 m thick unit of red marl with thin sandstone that passes up abruptly into a 79 m thick sandstone which fines upwards into a red, locally anhydritic, claystone/siltstone sequence containing a 496 m thick halite. A Norian to Rhaetian argillaceous sequence above the halite is overlain by a 29 m thick, grey, partly calcareous Rhaetian claystone that is lithologically similar to the top Triassic succession in the Melville Basin, except that the 'White Lias' limestone is not developed.

No drilling has taken place in the Shelf Edge Basin. Strong, parallel seismic reflectors near the base of this graben (Figure 30) are similar to those produced by the 'Liassic Limestone' in the Fastnet Basin (Robinson et al., 1981), and a suite of parallel reflectors with a truncated top beneath these reflectors may be of Permo-Triassic age.

The Cockburn Basin (Figure 33) is faulted along all sides except the north (N J P Smith, 1985). The basal unconformity is at a maximum depth of almost 5 km and at least a kilometre of Permo-Triassic strata is preserved. Comparison of the seismic signature of the sequence with that in surrounding basins suggests that it lacks a halite unit and is dominated by shale with some coarser sediment near the base.

The Permo-Triassic succession in the Fastnet Basin is generally much less than a kilometre thick, and a thickness of 615 m has been drilled in well 64/2-1 (Robinson et al.,

1981) from the Irish sector. The sequence consists of aeolian and fluvial sandstones at the base, passing up into shaly marl of a sabkha or lacustrine origin. Evaporites are present within the sandstones, which suggests that the sequence is Late Triassic in age.

7 Jurassic

A thick succession of mostly marine Jurassic sediments is preserved in the southern basins of the Western Approaches Trough and the South Celtic Sea Basin. However, in the northern basins of the Western Approaches Trough, Jurassic sediments are restricted to Liassic marine shales and limestones occupying two open synclines in the Melville Basin, and to the area south and east of the Plymouth Bay Basin where there is a highly faulted sequence of Lower to Middle Jurassic sediments. The lithology and facies of the Jurassic sequences offshore are similar to those preserved onshore in southern Britain. The present limited distribution of Jurassic rocks across these basins and the surrounding basement highs is largely the result of uplift and erosion during Late Jurassic to Early Cretaceous time. Because of this hiatus, the Middle to Late Jurassic palaeogeography of the northern basins of the Western Approaches Trough is inferred from sequences preserved in the surrounding basins.

A global eustatic transgression that commenced during the Late Triassic (Haq et al., 1987) introduced marine conditions across the low-lying basinal areas of the region by Rhaetian time, and these conditions persisted almost uninterrupted into the Middle Jurassic. This transgression brought about a change in sedimentation from the redbeds that dominated the Triassic to shallow-marine conditions with carbonate deposition during late Rhaetian and early Hettangian times. The Liassic sediments were deposited during a transgressive episode characterised by an irregular rise in sea level of between 75 and 110 m (Hallam, 1981). A change to slightly deeper water conditions during Sinemurian to Aalenian time resulted in the accumulation of shales with minor carbonate alternations. An estimated 2000 m of relatively uniform Liassic shale and limestone were deposited in the Melville Basin, indicating that the rates of sedimentation and subsidence remained approximately in balance through the Early Jurassic, which was a tectonically quiescent time of slow, continuous subsidence across the region.

Shallow-marine shales with minor sands and carbonates were deposited during the Middle Jurassic. Episodes of erosion and nondeposition of Bathonian to Oxfordian age are locally developed in the Celtic Sea and Bristol Channel basins (Millson, 1987), and similar events are recorded from the southern basins of the Western Approaches Trough. The regressions may be partially of tectonic origin, and are collectively equivalent to the mid-Cimmerian event in the North Sea (Ziegler, 1975). The intrusion of dolerite sills at the Bajocian–Bathonian boundary in the Fastnet Basin (Caston et al., 1981), the Callovian to Bathonian basaltic andesite flows in the Goban Spur (Cook, 1987), and the volcanically derived Fullers Earth deposits of Bathonian age in southern England, are related to the same crustal stresses that produced the tectonic uplift.

By the Late Jurassic, the regional doming of the area led to the creation of a more complex palaeogeography. There was uplift and erosion of some basins and rapid subsidence of other established basins, where substantial thicknesses of predominantly shallow-marine to evaporitic lagoonal shales accumulated.

The occurrence of Jurassic sediments on the floor of the easternmost part of the western English Channel was first demonstrated by dredging (Crawshay, 1908), and later surveys showed that these outcrops form structurally complex inliers along the eastern margin to the Western Approaches Trough (Curry et al., 1970). No Jurassic sediments crop out on the continental shelf to the west of 4°30′W, although their existence at depth was suggested prior to the deep drilling in the Western Approaches Trough by isolated samples of Upper Jurassic limestone dredged from the continental slope (Auffret et al., 1979).

The exploration for hydrocarbons in the sedimentary basins of the region has concentrated on structures involving presumed Jurassic strata, which are the source rocks in the nearest onshore oilfield at Wytch Farm (Colter and Havard, 1981) in Dorset (Figures 1 and 7). However, none of the wells in the northern basins of the Western Approaches Trough contain a succession as complete as that preserved onshore in southern England (Melville and Freshney, 1982).

LOWER JURASSIC

Lower Jurassic sediments are preserved in the Melville, Brittany, Southwest Channel and South Celtic Sea basins, as well as in the eastern part of the Plymouth Bay Basin; the alternating limestone and shale facies across the study area and its surrounds is comparatively uniform, implying deposition in a broad, shallow sea with little variation in water depth. However, the Cornubian Ridge was either barely emergent or an area of only limited deposition for at least part of the Early Jurassic. In the South Celtic Sea Basin, the carbonate content of the shales increases upwards within a series of 30 to 40 m thick cycles capped with limestone beds (Millson, 1987). These cycles may relate to minor eustatically induced regressions within the dominantly transgressive sequence (Hallam, 1981; Millson, 1987). Sands occur within the Sinemurian of the Fastnet Basin (Robinson et al., 1981), the Pliensbachian of the Bristol Channel Basin (Kamerling, 1979) and the Middle Lias of the Wessex Basin in southern England, but are less abundant in the wells drilled in the Western Approaches Trough. The source of these sands was probably the ancient massifs of Armorica and Cornubia, for there is no evidence of a major landmass immediately west of the trough at the time (Ziegler, 1987c).

In the Melville Basin, Liassic sediments occupy the cores of two irregularly shaped, east-north-east-trending synclinal structures (Figures 26 and 35) which owe their preservation to salt withdrawal during the Late Jurassic. Well 72/10-1A (Figure 8) proved 57 m of Lower Jurassic sediments between Penarth Group claystone and late Aptian volcanics. The base of the sequence is taken at a 10 m-thick limestone which is equated with the 'White Lias' of southern England (Bennet et al., 1985). The sequence passes up into dark grey, calcareous, marine claystone interbedded with micritic limestone of Hettangian age. In Well 73/1-1 the preserved sequence is lithologically similar but 498 m thick, and ranges in age from Hettangian to

Sinemurian; a 15 m-thick sandstone within this unit has not been recognised in other wells from the area. The Jurassic sediments are faulted against the Cornubian Platform to the north and west (Figures 26 and 35); most of the movement along these faults occurred during the Late Jurassic to Early Cretaceous (Hall, 1986), and there is no evidence for syndepositional faulting.

The lithological uniformity of the preserved strata in the region suggests that similar sediments may have been deposited in the St Mary's and Plymouth Bay basins, but were largely removed by subsequent erosion. The Jurassic sediments in the vicinity of well 88/2-1 are at least 650 m thick (Evans et al., 1981), and Curry et al. (1970) suggest that a maximum of 1000 m is preserved in the western English Channel. The sequence is lithologically similar to the Lias exposed on the Dorset coast, but is about twice as thick. Well 88/2-1 (Evans et al., 1981), drilled in a half-graben in the eastern part of the Plymouth Bay Basin, proved a 491 m-thick sequence of Hettangian to Pliensbachian, pale grey, fissile, marine mudstone and shale that is partly brown and carbonaceous, and contains thin beds of limestone in the lower part. The basal 35 m of the section is a pale grey to white, fine-grained limestone including abundant bands of fibrous calcite ('beef'). Geochemical evaluation shows that the sediments have a moderate to good potential to source hydrocarbons, but no arenaceous equivalents of the Pliensbachian sands and silts of the south Dorset coast occur in the section.

Lithologically more variable Lower Jurassic sequences are preserved in the southern basins of the Western Approaches Trough, where they locally rest on basement (Ziegler, 1987b). In the Southwest Channel Basin, the Lower Jurassic section is 33 m thick in Lennket-1 and consists of argillaceous arkose and dolomite passing up into feldpathic sandstone; this is overlain by argillaceous dolomite which extends into the Middle Jurassic. To the southwest, in the Brittany Basin, well Lizenn-1 terminated in a 149 m-thick section of greyish black to brown micrite with anhydrite of Hettangian to Sinemurian age. This passes up into a 1477 m-thick argillaceous unit whose top is of Bathonian (Middle Jurassic) age. In well Brezell-1, farther west in the basin, a 32 m-thick, fine-grained, Lower Jurassic arkosic sand rests on Permian sands, and passes up into a typical Liassic section of grey and black shales with micrite that is over 688 m thick.

A thick Lower to Middle Jurassic section is preserved in the core of the major east-north-east-trending synclinal structure that defines the South Celtic Sea Basin (Van Hoorn, 1987). Well 93/6-1 proved 40 m of Lower Jurassic grey mudstone resting on Rhaetian sediments. Although well 93/2-1 terminated in a 669 m-thick grey mudstone sequence of Bajocian to Bathonian age, seismic profiles across the site suggest that this sequence is underlain by a thick Lower Jurassic section (Van Hoorn, 1987).

MIDDLE JURASSIC

The palaeogeography of Early Jurassic time persisted into the Middle Jurassic, with the preserved record showing accumulations dominated by shale and limestone sequences. Towards the end of the epoch, there was a regional regression related to a tectonic pulse that also affected the North Sea Basin. A shallowing during Aalenian to Bathonian time led to the accumulation of sandstone and carbonate sequences of this age in the North Celtic Sea Basin. This was followed by the deposition of arenaceous sediments, and a widespread break in sedimentation during the late Bathonian. Late Jurassic to Early Cretaceous erosion has removed almost all Middle and Upper Jurassic strata from the Melville, St Mary's and Plymouth Bay basins. The only recorded Middle Jurassic sediment in these basins is the pale grey clay and calcarenite of late Bathonian to early Callovian age that crops out at sea bed 24 km west of Alderney in an inlier between the Southwest Channel and Plymouth Bay basins (Curry et al., 1970; Andreieff and Lefort, 1972).

The Late Jurassic erosional episode was not as severe in the Brittany and Southwest Channel basins where a more complete Middle to Upper Jurassic succession is preserved. To the east in well Lennket-1, there is a 187 m section of Lower to Middle Jurassic argillaceous dolomite, locally fissured and silicified, with galena mineralisation. This unit is overlain disconformably by sediments of Oxfordian to Kimmeridgian age. In the Brittany Basin to the west, the thick sequence of Middle Jurassic shale and limestone is lithologically similar to the Lower Jurassic. Siltstone passing up into medium- to coarse-grained sandstone occurs in the late Bathonian sequence from well Lizenn-1, and an unconformity of this age is recognised in well Brezell-1.

In the southern part of the South Celtic Sea Basin, well 93/2-1 terminated in a 669 m thick, uniform sequence of Bathonian and Bajocian dark grey, calcareous, silty mudstone. This unit is overlain unconformably by Early Cretaceous sediments with a nonmarine Wealden affinity. The Middle Jurassic erosional episode is therefore not recognised in this well but has been found in other wells in the northern part of the basin (Kamerling, 1979) and also in the Fastnet Basin, where Bathonian sands are overlain by Kimmeridgian carbonates (Robinson et al., 1981).

UPPER JURASSIC

Upper Jurassic sequences are preserved only in the Southwest Channel and Brittany basins and, to the north of the Cornubian Platform, in the Celtic Sea basins (Millson, 1987). In the Southwest Channel Basin, the Upper Jurassic is represented in well Lennket-1 by over 800 m of Oxfordian to Portlandian, shallow-marine to brackish-water argillaceous siltstone, locally brown and green, with minor intercalations of anhydrite, and some medium- to coarse-grained sandstone. Rare anhydritic layers occur in the upper part of the unit. The base of the unit is separated from the underlying Middle Jurassic dolomite at a depositional hiatus. An Upper Jurassic unit of similar lithology is found in the Brittany Basin, and in both basins the sequence passes up into Cretaceous sediments with no depositional break.

The age of the major uplift and erosion of the Jurassic sequences across the northern basins of the Western Approaches Trough is difficult to date because of the great age range of the associated hiatus. Well 87/12-1, drilled to the north of the Ouessant–Alderney fault zone separating the Brittany and St Mary's basins, proved Upper Jurassic to Lower Cretaceous fresh- to brackish-water mudstone and sandstone of probable Portlandian to Berriasian age resting unconformably on Triassic mudstone. The bulk of the erosion therefore occurred during or before the Portlandian, and regional considerations suggest erosion of the area throughout much of the Late Jurassic.

Within the Celtic Sea basins, the Upper Jurassic consists of a complex series of interfingering fluvial and high-energy, marginal-marine sediments. Jurassic sea level reached a peak during the Oxfordian to Kimmeridgian, but sea levels across the region during the Late Jurassic became dominated more by local tectonic influences than eustatic changes (Millson, 1987), with uplift to the west introducing substantial clastic sediments into a subsiding basin in which eustatic sea level was also rising. Upper Jurassic sediments have been removed from the southern part of the South Celtic Sea Basin, but a sequence at least 90 m thick is preserved in the north-eastern part of the basin and is even thicker in the Bristol Channel Basin (Kamerling, 1979).

During the Late Jurassic, a carbonate platform sequence accumulated in intertidal to bathyal environments across the present Western Approaches and Bay of Biscay margins as far north as 48°N (Auffret et al., 1979). The development of these reefs and the disappearance westwards of anhydrite in the Upper Jurassic of the Brittany Basin are indicative of more open-marine conditions at this time in a narrow rift-basin immediately west of the Western Approaches Trough (Zeigler, 1987c). This basin was the precursor of the oceanic basin that formed in the area during the Early Cretaceous.

THE MIDDLE JURASSIC TO EARLY CRETACEOUS EROSIONAL EVENTS

A series of minor, widespread erosional events of late Middle to earliest Late Jurassic age are recognised across the region. They are divisible into a minor regional uplift/disconformity in the late Middle to early Late Jurassic, and a much more significant uplift and erosional event during the Late Jurassic that was centred on the Cornubian Ridge and adjacent Mesozoic sedimentary basins.

Millson (1987) correlates one of the events in the north Celtic Sea with the deposition of a distinctive late Batho-nian to earliest Callovian nonmarine redbed unit that unconformably overlies older strata. However, the full extent of this unconformity is uncertain, for in the western part of the North Celtic Sea Basin a pre-late Oxfordian unconformity truncates Middle Jurassic sediments. In the eastern part of the South Celtic Sea Basin, Kimmeridgian to Portlandian dolomitic and silty limestones disconformably overlie Callovian siltstones, although no angular discordance is evident on seismic profiles.

The pulse of Late Jurassic to Early Cretaceous uplift and erosion was most vigorous across the Melville, St Mary's and Plymouth Bay basins in the Western Approaches Trough, and in the South Celtic Sea Basin. Most of the Jurassic strata, with a thickness that may have exceeded 2000 m locally, have been removed from the northern basins of the Western Approaches Trough. The outliers in the Melville Basin owe their preservation to the development of lows as a result of salt withdrawal associated with halokinesis during the uplift phase. The age of the uplift is uncertain, for the youngest sediments underneath the erosion surface in the Melville Basin are of Sinemurian age. Each basin reacted differently to the tectonic events of the time; while the northern basins of the trough were uplifted and their Jurassic infill removed, subsidence continued and increased in magnitude across the southern basins (see Chapter 5). These uplift events relate to a series of tectonic pulses which are not synchronous across the region. The pulses are linked to rifting in the Bay of Biscay and the opening of the North Atlantic (Ziegler, 1987c); these continued into the Early Cretaceous, though the main uplift and erosion of the northern basins of the Western Approaches Trough had reached its peak by the end of Jurassic time.

8 Cretaceous

Tectonic instability during the Late Jurassic and Early Cretaceous produced uplift and erosion across the Western Approaches Trough. This resulted in the removal of most of the Jurassic strata from the northern basins where Cretaceous rocks now rest with marked unconformity on the underlying sequences. The Early Cretaceous strata consist of a thin sequence of shallow-marine clastics with some volcanic rocks, usually resting on Permo-Triassic or Lower Jurassic sediments. Locally, a thin sequence of fluviolacustrine Wealden facies clastics is preserved beneath the marine sediments.

In the Brittany and Southwest Channel basins, deposition proceeded from the Jurassic into the Cretaceous with no significant break, and a thick sequence of shallow-marine sediments accumulated during the Early Cretaceous. Hillis (1988) argues that although there was regional uplift during this time, these southern basins were subjected to localised subsidence which was of greater magnitude than the uplift; thus sediments continued to accumulate in these basins while erosion dominated to the north. The regional uplift was associated with crustal events which led to the extension and ultimate break up of the crust from the Bay of Biscay to the Goban Spur during the Aptian to Albian. During this break up, the environment of the present middle and lower continental slope changed abruptly from shallow marine to bathyal.

The eustatic sea-level rise which had begun at the start of the Cretaceous reached a maximum during the Cenomanian to Turonian. Sea level remained high, about 200 to 350 m above the present level, into the early Tertiary and started to fall during the Oligocene (Haq et al., 1987). This led to the deposition during the Late Cretaceous of a blanket of chalk, locally over 500 m thick, covering the basinal areas and most of the adjacent massifs. Tectonic subsidence of the region following the earlier uplift contributed to the accumulation of these thick sequences. Deposition was less continuous on the subsiding continental slope and outer shelf where a major hiatus is recorded between Lower and Upper Cretaceous strata.

LOWER CRETACEOUS

Lower Cretaceous strata crop out locally at the sea bed along the margins of the Western Approaches Trough, though the outcrop pattern is discontinuous due to both faulting and overstep by later units (Figure 3). The thin but continuous Aptian to Albian succession preserved beneath the Upper Cretaceous cover along its northern margin was sampled both by drilling (Lott et al., 1980) and gravity coring (Wilkinson and Halliwell, 1980). Curry et al. (1970) noted a large outlier of Lower Cretaceous sediments to the south-west of the Hurd Deep composed of sandstone, arkose and clay of terrestrial aspect, and estimated that the unit was about 150 m thick. Lower Cretaceous sections from some of the wells in the Western Approaches Trough are shown in Figure 37; inter-well correlations across the region are limited both by lithological changes and the variability of the biostratigraphic data.

Berriasian to Valanginian

Sediments of Berriasian to Valanginian age have a restricted distribution, and are thickest in the southern basins of the Western Approaches Trough where sedimentation continued from the Jurassic into the Cretaceous with no major break. Rocks of this age are also found in the North Celtic Sea and Fastnet basins, and under the continental slope. In the Southwest Channel Basin, the Neocomian (Berriasian to Hauterivian) unit is about 1200 m thick and consists of multicoloured sandy clay, with medium- to coarse-grained, lignitic, locally pyritised sand. The basal part of the unit is a silty clay of Berriasian age and displays a freshwater facies similar to the middle and upper Purbeck in Dorset. The Berriasian to Valanginian unit is only 40 m thick in well Lizenn-1, but thickens south-westwards to nearly 300 m in well Brezell-1. To the north, well 87/12-1A recovered a similar facies of ?Portlandian to Berriasian age resting on Triassic sediments (Figure 37).

To the north of the report area, Berriasian to Valanginian fluvial and alluvial sandstones of Wealden facies up to 500 m thick are found in the Fastnet and North Celtic Sea basins, and Valanginian sediments are known from the southern part of the North Celtic Sea Basin (Robinson et al., 1981; Ainsworth et al., 1987). An unconformity at the margins of the Fastnet Basin separates the Wealden facies from the overlying Aptian to Cenomanian marine facies. DSDP site 401 on the continental slope (Figure 1) proved nearshore, micritised, reefal limestone and algal lumps of Jurassic to late Aptian age (Montadert et al., 1979). This unit forms part of a reef system which developed prior to the breakup of the continental margin on the eastern, landward margin of the rift basin (Masson and Roberts, 1981).

Hauterivian to Barremian

Shallow-marine to brackish and freshwater sedimentation continued in the southern basins of the Western Approaches Trough through the Hauterivian and Barremian, and also encroached northwards as a precursor to the series of transgressions which covered the whole Western Approaches Trough during the Aptian and Albian. In the southern basins, the Hauterivian to Barremian sequence consists of fluvial to brackish-water, locally dolomitic, multicoloured mudstones with sandstones. The sequence is over 300 m thick in well Brezell-1 where the lower part contains lignite and the upper section is locally an oolitic limestone, denoting the incoming of marine influence. The northward transgression at this time is recorded in wells 85/28-1 and 86/18-1 where a thin Barremian sequence of white, pyritic and carbonaceous sand with pale to dark grey claystone rests on Triassic sediments. A lithologically similar, 113 m-thick sequence occurs in well 73/7-1 in the Melville Basin.

Lott et al. (1980) describe a Barremian to pre-Middle Albian section about 20 m thick from a borehole (SLS 16) drilled east-south-east of the Lizard (Figure 7), although most boreholes in the area proved Middle Albian sediment resting on Permo-Triassic strata. The unit consists of grey

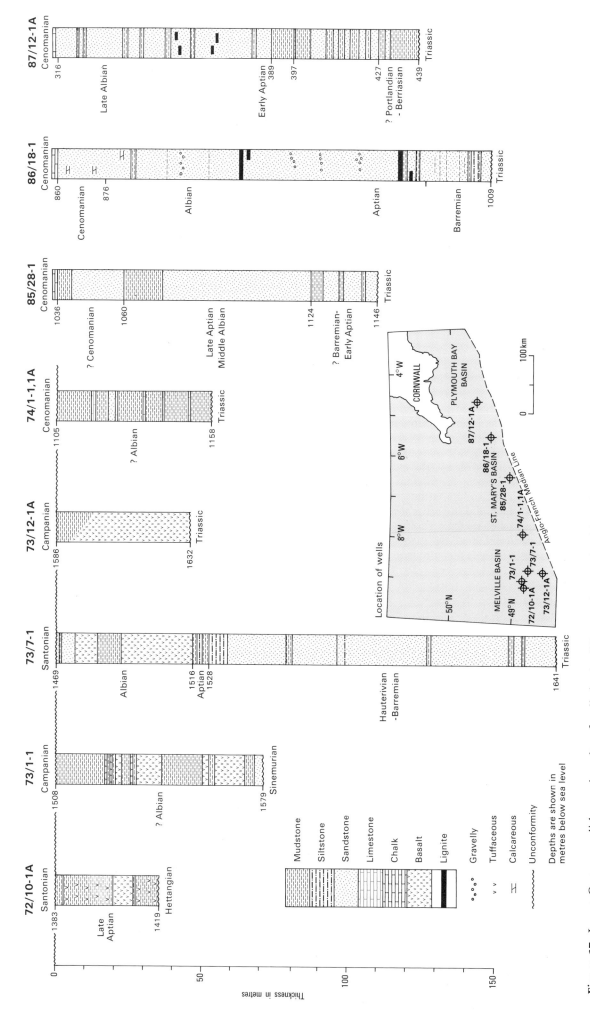

Figure 37 Lower Cretaceous lithostratigraphy of wells in the Western Approaches Trough. Age ranges are given where known.

54

and white clay with fine sand, cut by coarse, carbonaceous, channel-fill sand deposited under marine influence but near a terrestrial source. Shallow seismic evidence suggests that the unit forms localised infill sequences up to 100 m thick.

Kamerling (1979) records an unconformity between Berriasian redbeds and Aptian sediments in the northern part of the South Celtic Sea Basin. Well 93/2-1 from the basin recorded a 277 m-thick Aptian and undifferentiated Early Cretaceous deltaic sandstone and mudstone sequence with lignite. Freshwater or shallow-marine sediments of Hauterivian to Barremian age are recorded in the Fastnet and North Celtic Sea basins; the marine influence is stronger in the southern parts of the basins (Ainsworth et al., 1987).

A series of rapidly subsiding half-grabens formed under the present continental slope during the Hauterivian to Barremian in response to the tectonic forces that ultimately led to the creation of oceanic crust in the newly formed proto-Atlantic. DSDP site 549 was drilled into a wedge of mostly Barremian sediment within such a half-graben on the Goban Spur continental slope. At the site, the wedge contains 291 m of grey, red and yellow sandstone with some limestone and mudstone that were deposited in a low-energy, littoral environment which became progressively more marine. The base of the sequence has a late Hauterivian or early Barremian age (Müller, 1985), which dates the onset of half-graben formation. The top of the sequence is of late Barremian age, and is terminated at the discontinuity marking the end of crustal stretching and the onset of sea-floor spreading in the adjacent ocean. This hiatus between late Barremian and early Albian sediments was the result of rotation and tilting of the fault-block forming the half-graben, raising the sequence above sea level. On the Western Approaches margin, thin shallow marine limestones (site 401) accumulated during the late Berriasian to late Aptian, and there is little evidence for the erosion of tilted-block crests recorded farther north.

The rifting on the margin was accompanied by isolated volcanism on the shelf (see p. 56). The volcanic plugs forming Wolf Rock and Epson Shoal were intruded between Berriasian and Aptian time (130 to 112 Ma) (Harrison et al., 1977), and Ziegler (1987b) notes late Neocomian to Barremian sills in the Brittany Basin.

Aptian to Albian

Shallow-marine conditions continued to spread across the shelf during the Aptian, with the deposition of a shallow-water sandstone sequence onto the Late Jurassic to Early Cretaceous erosion surface across the northern basins of the Western Approaches Trough. During the early Aptian, a renewed phase of tectonism affected the trough, briefly interrupting sedimentation in the southern basins and leading to the removal of much of the earlier Cretaceous sediment in the northern basins (Ziegler, 1987b). In well 85/28-1, the basal ?Barremian to early Aptian sequence of carbonaceous sandstone and claystone is 22 m thick and is overlain by 64 m of late Aptian to middle Albian sandstone topped by glauconitic claystone (Figure 37). In the Melville Basin, the Aptian sandstone in well 73/8-1 contains volcaniclastic input; similar input extends up into sediments of Albian age in other wells from the basin. Deposition also continued during this interval in the southern basins of the trough; 205 m of grey to black and brown silt, locally lignitic and glauconitic, were recovered from well Lizenn-1.

By Albian time, the transgression had extended across the whole Western Approaches Trough and onto the margins of the Cornubian Platform. Lott et al. (1980) recognise three lithostratigraphic units within the Lower Cretaceous on the flanks of the Western Approaches Trough. The basal unit of Wealden facies, and of Barremian to pre-middle Albian age, has been described above. The overlying two units are of middle to late Albian age; these more widespread units rest with marked unconformity on underlying rocks across the western and southern flanks of the Cornubian Platform. The lower unit consists of up to 15 m of dark grey to black, sandy, carbonaceous clay of middle Albian age deposited in quiet water with deoxygenated bottom conditions. Renewed transgression, perhaps interrupted by a minor regression, introduced true marine conditions into the area and resulted in the deposition of the upper unit, a massive limestone up to 21 m thick (SLS 74) of late Albian to early Cenomanian age. This limestone locally contains pebbly, bioclastic mudstone with an impoverished foraminiferal population, and passes eastwards into a pale grey, medium- to coarse-grained sandstone up to 65 m thick (SLS 64 and 64X) containing a rich dinoflagellate cyst assemblage of late Albian age. These Albian limestones and sandstones pass up into the Chalk; in the north-western English Channel, the basal Chalk is of Turonian age and rests disconformably on late Albian to early Cenomanian sandstone. Over the Cornubian Platform the youngest Chalk is of late or possibly mid-Cenomanian age, and in wells 86/18-1 and 87/12-1A the late Albian sandstone extends into the Cenomanian.

Lott et al. (1980) established a correlation between the Aptian to Albian units on the fringes of the Cornubian Platform and those on the continental margin (de Graciansky et al., 1987). The black carbonaceous clays of middle Albian age from the eastern part of the Western Approaches Trough have been recognised at a number of localities on the North Atlantic margin. They are indicative of an anoxic event that developed when the newly formed proto-North Atlantic was relatively shallow and had a poorly developed circulation system (de Graciansky et al., 1987).

Seismic profiles indicate little change in the geometry of the Aptian to Albian unit in the deeper parts of the northern basins within the Western Approaches Trough. The sequence in the St Mary's and Plymouth Bay basins and in the western part of the Melville Basin is usually less than 100 m thick, and consists of alternations of pyritic, glauconitic sandstone with dark grey claystone (Figure 37). The Albian is thicker in the Southwest Channel Basin, and well Lizenn-1 recorded a 300 m-thick section that contains lignitic intercalations, indicating that fully marine conditions did not enter this basin until the late Albian.

Lower Cretaceous strata are absent from wells 88/2-1 and 87/14-1 in the eastern Plymouth Bay Basin, where Cenomanian limestone rests directly on pre-Cretaceous sediments. In the adjacent well 87/16-1, 38 m of dark greyish brown, carbonaceous Albian mudstone with fine- to medium-grained sand separates the Chalk from Triassic mudstone.

On the outer shelf, volcanic intercalations occur beneath and within the argillaceous or arenaceous Aptian to Albian succession in a series of wells up to 40 km apart lying about 40 km landward of the present shelf edge (Figures 8 and 37). The volcanic rocks consist of at least 35 m of hard, greenish black, porphyritic, olivine-rich basalts with a trachytic texture and some veins of talc (Bennet et al., 1985). The basalts also display a variolitic texture and are locally weathered to a mottled white to medium grey and greyish red colour. They are locally vesicular and display intense haematisation in parts. Waxy, greenish grey claystone passing up into a red-brown claystone is interbedded with the basalt. The weathered basalt tops suggest deposition under terrestrial conditions, with perhaps local shallow-water influence indicated by the variolitic texture. In wells 73/1-1 and 73/7-1, the volcanics are interbedded with sediments of possible Albian age, whereas in wells 73/8-1 and 72/10-1A the intercalated sediments are Aptian.

Early Cretaceous tectonism formed the South Celtic Sea Basin into its present narrow, elongate shape (Colin et al., 1981), and the Chalk is underlain by a Lower Cretaceous unit of variable thickness. In well 93/6-1, 19 m of Lower Cretaceous, grey, calcareous claystone pass down into a fine sandstone which rests unconformably on Lower Jurassic claystone. By contrast, well 93/2-1 proved a 277 m-thick sand, mudstone and lignite unit (Wealden facies) of Aptian and undifferentiated Early Cretaceous age, overlain by a 19 m-thick middle Albian section of similar lithology succeeded by 52 m of grey, silty, calcareous mudstone (Gault facies) of late Albian age.

The stretching of the continental margin, which began during the Hauterivian, reached a climax during the Aptian to Albian. Stretching of the continental crust ceased and the fault-blocks underlying the half graben stopped moving when sea-floor spreading commenced in the newly formed oceanic basin. This took place during the Aptian on the Western Approaches margin (Montadert et al., 1979) and in Albian times on the Goban Spur margin (de Graciansky and Poag, 1985). Site 402A on the Western Approaches margin recovered 294 m of early Aptian to late Albian limestone, mudstone and chalk formed in water depths of between 50 and 400 m on a carbonate platform probably aligned along the crest of a fault block (Roberts and Montadert, 1979). Following cessation of crustal stretching, the area began to subside rapidly, and sank to bathyal depths during the Late Cretaceous.

Lower Cretaceous volcanic rocks have been dredged from Shamrock Canyon on the continental slope (Pastouret et al., 1981). Volcanic rocks are absent from the DSDP boreholes on the Goban Spur (de Graciansky and Poag, 1985), although their presence in the area is suspected from gravity and magnetic data (Cook, 1987).

Early Cretaceous igneous intrusions

Wolf Rock, an island no more than 60 m across which lies about 15 km south-west of Land's End at 49°56′N 5°47′W (Figure 1), is formed of fine-grained, fluxioned, microporphyritic phonolite (Harrison et al., 1977). The nearby Epson Shoal (49°57′N 5°38′W) is formed of similar strongly fluxioned phonolite. K-Ar age determinations on the intrusions gave mean ages of 112 ± 2 Ma and 130 ± 6 Ma (Berriasian to Aptian) respectively. The shapes of the bodies and their igneous textures suggest that they are volcanic necks; this alkaline magmatism may be associated with contemporary rifting at this time along the Ouessant–Alderney fault zone, or with movement along a major wrench fault system which displaces the Cornubian Batholith, and may have been active during the Early Cretaceous (Hillis, 1988).

Sills of late Neocomian to Barremian age in the Brittany Basin (Ziegler, 1987b) are of similar age to the Wolf Rock, but may be more closely related to the volcanic rocks of Aptian to Albian age on the outer shelf whose source is uncertain. A possible centre for the outer shelf volcanics is

a circular magnetic anomaly at 48°42′N 9°16′W, about 30 km west of the wells which recorded the basalts in the Melville Basin; this anomaly differs from others in the area in having a sharp rather than a flat top (Figure 21). A seismic profile at the site shows a high level complex of diffractors and dipping reflectors overlain by a thick, undisturbed, post-Early Cretaceous sequence.

Magnetic anomalies to the north-west of Haig Fras, about 1 km outside the granite margin, coincide with low south-south-east-trending sea-bed ridges. These anomalies can be modelled as a suite of basic dykes displaying both normal and reversed polarisation. The magnetic characteristics of the dykes suggest a Mesozoic or Tertiary age, but the trend is normal to the Tertiary suite in south-west Ireland and around Lundy, suggesting that they may be of Mesozoic age.

UPPER CRETACEOUS

Generally high sea levels during the Late Cretaceous led to the deposition of a blanket of Chalk with flints up to several hundred metres thick across the region (Tyson and Funnell, 1987). This cover is presently thickest across the early Mesozoic basinal area, as it has been eroded off landward portions of the basement highs, and severely thinned on their flanks. Early Cretaceous sediments are missing across some parts of the Cornubian Platform where the Chalk rests directly on the Late Jurassic to Early Cretaceous erosion surface (BGS Haig Fras–Labadie Bank Solid Geology sheet). The uppermost part of the Chalk is within the Paleocene (Danian), but the top is an erosion surface, and Danian chalk is preserved only in parts of the Melville Basin and the eastern Plymouth Bay Basin.

The base of the Upper Cretaceous (Figure 38) extends south-westwards onto the continental slope with no significant change in attitude for up to 25 km beyond the indented shelfbreak (Figure 14). Oceanward of this zone, the Upper Cretaceous drapes over the middle and lower slope fault-block topography that was created during the Early Cretaceous. Condensed sections of Upper Cretaceous strata have been recovered from the continental slope (Auffret et al., 1979; de Graciansky and Poag, 1985).

The nearest extensive onshore Chalk is a 110 m-thick Cenomanian to Turonian section in south-east Devon (Edmonds et al., 1975). Residual deposits of Santonian to Campanian age are found as far west as the Haldon Hills (Figure 38) east of Dartmoor (Selwood et al., 1984), but the higher parts of the Cornubian and Armorican massifs may have remained emergent throughout the Late Cretaceous (Tyson and Funnell, 1987).

The Chalk is exposed at sea bed in a broad zone around south-west England, and in a less complete arc off north-west France (Figure 3). Curry et al. (1970) and Boillot et al. (1972) demonstrated that most of the Chalk at sea bed is Santonian or older to the south and west of the Isles of Scilly, but is Campanian or younger around the eastern closure of the Western Approaches Trough, except where Cenomanian strata crop out along the northern margin. Along the south-eastern flanks of the Western Approaches Trough, the basal Upper Cretaceous oversteps onto the Armorican Massif. During the Cenomanian, the south-eastern limit of deposition lay near the centre of the trough in the English Channel, but as sea level rose it moved southwards until Chalk sedimentation extended to cover the northern part of the Cotentin Peninsula and the Channel Islands in Maastrichtian time (Donovan, 1972). The Chalk was deposited across an area which at the start of the

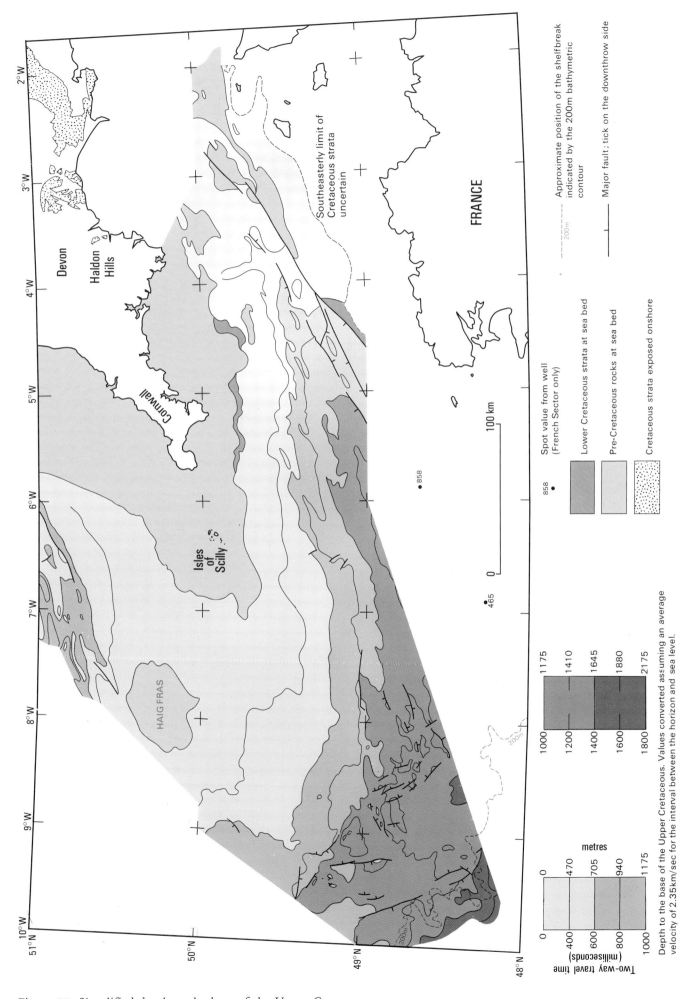

Figure 38 Simplified depth to the base of the Upper Cretaceous.

57

transgression had a low, mature relief, and only locally do seismic profiles show the basal sequence onlapping topographic features. The slow progress of the transgression southwards over Brittany and the Cotentin Peninsula may indicate that the Armorican Massif was at that time an area of higher relief than Cornubia, in contrast to the present where the reverse is true (Durrance and Bristow, 1986). A hypothetical geometrical construction on the northern limb of the Western Approaches Trough south of Cornwall suggests that the base of the Chalk was at an altitude of about 200 m above present-day south Cornwall (see Durrance and Bristow, 1986). The present relief is due to subsequent tectonic warping of the area, so palaeogeographic reconstructions of Chalk limits should not be too strongly influenced by the present elevations of the massifs.

The curve of sea-level change proposed by Hancock and Kauffman (1979) shows a steady rise of about 350 m from the Albian to the Campanian, with a minor regression during Turonian to Santonian time and an abrupt fall in the late Maastrichtian. By contrast, Haq et al. (1987) show the eustatic sea-level curve at an almost uniformly high level through the Late Cretaceous but with a series of lowstands, the most important of which occurred during the late Turonian and late Maastrichtian. Biostratigraphic evidence indicates that water depths across the present shelf area were less than 200 m for the whole of the period and probably less than 100 m for much of that time. Accumulation of the Chalk therefore kept pace with the rising sea level and/or crustal subsidence to keep the contemporary water depth reasonably constant. The geometry of the seismic reflectors also indicates deposition on a relatively stable continental platform, with no evidence across the present shelf for substantial deepening of the sea towards the newly formed Atlantic Ocean.

There are substantial variations in the thicknesses of the Upper Cretaceous stages between the wells drilled in the area, but the gross thickness of the unit is more constant (Figures 8 and 39). No significant lithological variation occurs within the Chalk across the Western Approaches Trough and the Cornubian Ridge, for both areas were part of the single depositional province during this period.

A major hiatus recognised at the base of the Upper Cretaceous across the outer shelf and continental slope appears to be the result of nondeposition rather than erosion. The limits of this zone of nondeposition retreated oceanward in Santonian time to disappear by the Maastrichtian and produce an oceanward downlapping sequence overlying the disconformity on the upper slope. This hiatus may have been due to the outer shelf/upper slope area being slightly elevated by tectonic and/or thermal processes related to the Early Cretaceous opening of the North Atlantic, or to vigorous oceanic currents at the margins of the newly formed North Atlantic Ocean.

The full succession of Chalk in the UK Sector of the Western Approaches Trough varies in thickness between 350 and 550 m; the sequences preserved over the early Mesozoic basins being slightly thicker than those on the flanks of the basement highs (Figures 8 and 39). The basal part of the transgressive sequence, which may include some Lower Cretaceous strata, fills broad depressions in the underlying erosion surface and onlaps against local highs and fault scarps, but these have minimal influence on the regional thickness of the unit. Some wells drilled in the Melville Basin are located on the flanks of halokinetic highs (Bennet et al., 1985); the Chalk shows no lithological or geometric changes across these highs, for the Late Jurassic halokinetic swells had been eroded prior to the

deposition of the Upper Cretaceous, and their present form is due to reactivation during mid-Tertiary halokinesis.

On seismic profiles, the Chalk displays continuous, parallel reflectors of variable continuity and amplitude generated by the hardgrounds, flint horizons and chalk/limestone alternations. Although the seismic reflectors are generally parallel or subparallel, there is an area centred about 45 km south of the Isles of Scilly where the reflectors display two levels of reefal banks and channels. The highly reflective basal Chalk of Turonian to Coniacian age is overlain by a sequence containing symmetrical mounds between 400 and 600 m across and up to 40 m high which occasionally have faint internal reflectors that show increased convexity with growth (Figure 40). The banks merge westward into Chalk with parallel-bedded reflectors. The chalk overlying these banks is at least as young as the early Campanian and contains an upper series of rounded, concentric, bank-like forms up to 1500 m across and 60 m high with slopes up to 9°. This style of reflectors covers an area of at least 3000 sq km, and similar structures of shallow-water reefal origin have been described by Kennedy and Juignet (1974) from the Turonian to Santonian Chalk of northern France. The shallowing of the seas that led to reefal development could have been due to a short-lived global lowering of sea level during the Turonian (Haq et al., 1987), or to a minor tectonic uplift.

The regional form of the base Upper Cretaceous (Figure 38) is significantly different from that of the base Permo-Triassic (Figure 33). The latter picks out the main sedimentary basins within the Western Approaches Trough, but only the major trend of the trough is obvious on the former. Figure 38 shows a broad east-north-east-trending syncline opening and deepening to the west-south-west. The northern margin is a smooth surface sloping gently off the Cornubian Platform into both the Western Approaches Trough and the Cockburn Basin. Increased faulting at the base Cretaceous level within the French Sector north of Brittany marks the faults separating the Brittany and Southwest Channel basins from those to the north (Ziegler, 1987b). Uplift and erosion of the southern basins during the Tertiary has resulted in the preservation of the thickest and most complete Upper Cretaceous successions in the northern part of the Western Approaches Trough. Minor faults (Figures 27 and 38) are mostly related to later halokenesis within the Melville Basin; faults defining the northern margin of the basin have not moved significantly since the Early Cretaceous.

The Chalk is generally about 350 m thick in the South Celtic Sea Basin, but penecontemporaneous salt movement has led to the local accumulation of much thicker sequences, with 844 m in well 93/2-1 drilled on the flank of a salt wall (Kamerling, 1979).

The Upper Cretaceous blanket generally thins to between 120 and 160 m in the Fastnet Basin (Robinson et al., 1981) and thickens northwards to over 820 m in the Kinsale Head area of the North Celtic Sea Basin (Colley et al., 1981). The decrease in thickness across the Fastnet Basin may be attributed to a phase of gentle inversion which began during the late Albian and continued at least until the middle Campanian (Colin et al., 1981; Robinson et al., 1981).

Lithology and stratigraphy of the Chalk

The unit consists of relatively soft, clay-like chalk grading down into hard limestone at the base, although a sandy basal Cenomanian facies is developed locally (Figure 31).

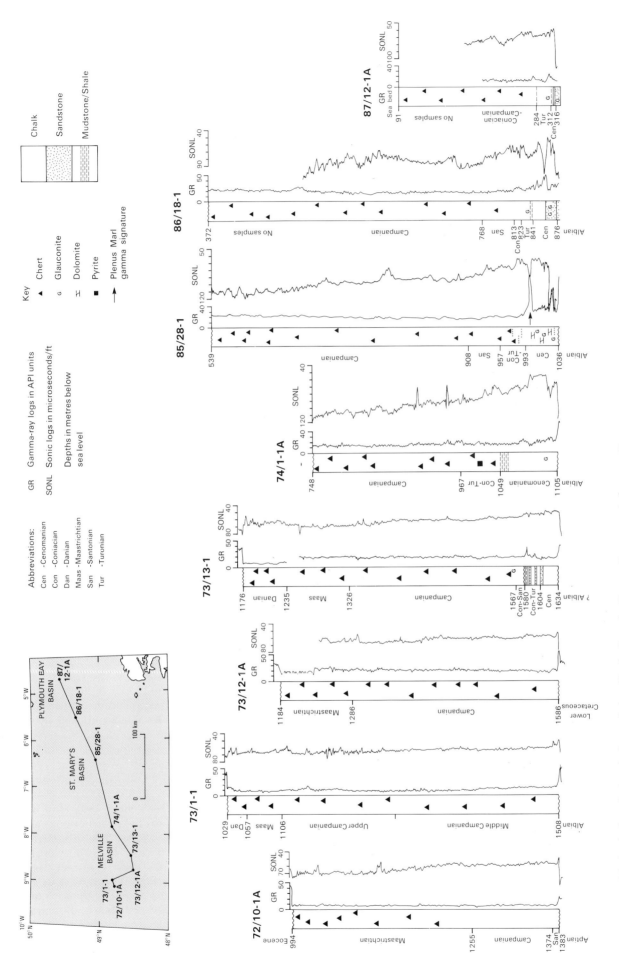

Figure 39 Lithological and electric logs of the Chalk (largely Upper Cretaceous) from wells in the Western Approaches Trough.

59

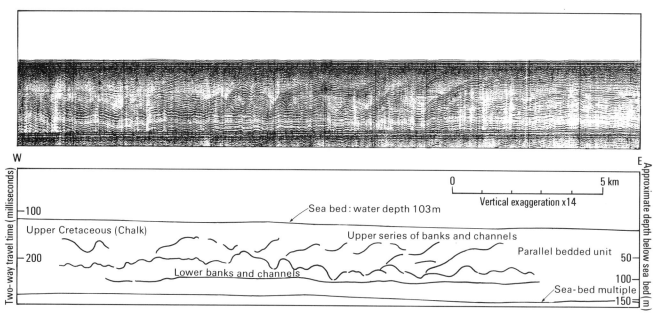

Figure 40 Seismic section through the Upper Cretaceous (Chalk) banks. For location see Figure 6.

The sonic logs show a steady upward decrease in sonic velocity from the Cenomanian to the Santonian; this rate of decrease diminishes appreciably in the thicker Campanian to Maastrichtian Chalk. The sonic velocity reflects the porosity of the Chalk; the decrease upwards is a function of a reduction in overburden.

Wells from the deeper parts of the St Mary's Basin have recovered an Upper Cretaceous sequence extending from the Cenomanian to the Maastrichtian. The lower part of this sequence is absent in the western Melville Basin, and mid-Tertiary erosion has removed part or all of the Chalk across the Plymouth Bay Basin. The lower stages of the Upper Cretaceous become thinner oceanward across the outer shelf so that near the shelfbreak the lower part is missing and the oldest sediments are Campanian (or Santonian) in age, resting directly on Lower Cretaceous volcaniclastics. Thus the Cenomanian to Santonian sequence thins between wells 74/1-1A and 73/13-1 and is absent in well 73/12-1A (Figure 31). This thickness variation of the stages has the form of a very gentle oceanward downlap, with the upper stages being thickest in the extreme south-western part of the shelf.

Cenomanian

In well 86/18-1, drilled in the centre of the Western Approaches Trough, the Cenomanian consists of 35 m of glauconitic, calcareous sand passing up abruptly into a hard crystalline chalky limestone with grey chert. To the east, the lithologies are similar in well 87/12-1A, but thicken locally to at least 67 m in well 87/14-1 where the top becomes chalky. A similar transition is recorded on the northern flanks of the trough, with the basal Cenomanian consisting of bioclastic limestone in the west and sandstone in the east, both passing up into Chalk (Lott et al., 1980). In borehole SLS 31A on the northern margin of the Plymouth Bay Basin, middle and upper Cenomanian sediments are absent, and Turonian Chalk rests non-sequentially on late Albian to early Cenomanian sandstone (Lott et al., 1980).

In south-east Devon, the Cenomanian is lithologically similar to that in the basin centre, although the facies is complex in detail and is influenced by both the elevation of the locality and penecontemporaneous tectonics (Edmonds et al., 1975). Heavy mineral analysis of these strata shows that the Dartmoor granite was largely unexposed during this time, though other Cornish granites were being eroded (Hancock, 1969).

Under the middle shelf, the Cenomanian is a pale brown, glauconitic limestone about 50 m thick. The Plenus Marl, an argillaceous bed recognised near the Cenomanian–Turonian boundary from the northern North Sea to the Goban Spur (Hart and Ball, 1986), gives a distinctive signature on some of the gamma-ray log traces such as well 85/28-1. This marl is also recognised in the Fastnet Basin where it overlies arenaceous Cenomanian strata (Robinson et al., 1981).

The Cenomanian extends as a glauconitic limestone into the western part of the Melville Basin, where it dies out and the younger units overstep south-westwards onto Lower Cretaceous strata. Cenomanian sediments reappear oceanward under the middle slope on the Goban Spur where DSDP site 549 recovered 52.4 m of greenish grey chalk of early Cenomanian to early Turonian age with a distinctive section of altered volcanic ash and black pyritic shale.

Turonian and Coniacian

The 98 m-thick Turonian section in east Devon is the youngest part of the Upper Cretaceous preserved in that area. It has a gritty limestone base and passes up into a nodular chalk that becomes very flinty.

The Turonian to Coniacian in well 86/18-1 in the western English Channel consists of 28 m of white to greyish yellow-green, crystalline, glauconitic limestone with rare chert. The unit thickens eastwards to 85 m in well 87/14-1 and the Turonian alone is 207 m thick in well 87/16-1 where flint becomes more abundant and there are traces of tan dolomite and pyrite. The Turonian retains a generally uniform thickness and lithology into the eastern part of the Melville Basin but thins westwards to a combined thickness with the Coniacian of a little more than 24 m in 73/13-1 where the Turonian to Santonian is chalk alternating with sand, shale and limestone, and there is an unconformity within the Coniacian.

No Turonian to Coniacian strata are found in the westernmost wells on the continental shelf, though about 18 m of pale greenish grey chalk of this age were proved on the middle slope of the Goban Spur at site 549 (de Graciansky and Poag, 1985).

Santonian to Maastrichtian

Faunas of Santonian or Campanian age derived from flints in the Haldon gravels north of Teignmouth (Edmonds et al., 1975) show that the Upper Cretaceous sea covered the eastern slopes of Dartmoor, though Tyson and Funnell (1987) suggest that the bulk of the Cornubian Massif remained uncovered through the Late Cretaceous. The Santonian to probable Maastrichtian section in well 86/18-1 from the western English Channel is 441 m thick and consists of white, firm chalk with brown flints (Figure 39). The Upper Campanian section is stylolitic, with dark green clay laminae, traces of pyrite and abundant fragments of bryozoa, foraminifera, and shells. To the east in well 87/14-1, the section thins to about 200 m and is overlain by Danian Chalk; to the west the unit is about 400 m on the outer shelf, where again the overlying Danian Chalk is preserved.

Under the outermost shelf, the oldest Santonian section (well 73/7-1) is white chalk interbedded with limestone and tan, glauconitic siltstone; these pass up into the ubiquitous chalk lithology. In this area there is no distinctive basal sequence to the Upper Cretaceous other than this lower glauconitic section which in 72/10-1A is a limestone some 9 m thick. On the Goban Spur margin, the Upper Cretaceous section at site 548 consists of 60 m of chalk of late Campanian to Danian age with a distinctive glauconitic, sideritic and phosphatic hardground at the base (de Graciansky and Bourbon, 1985).

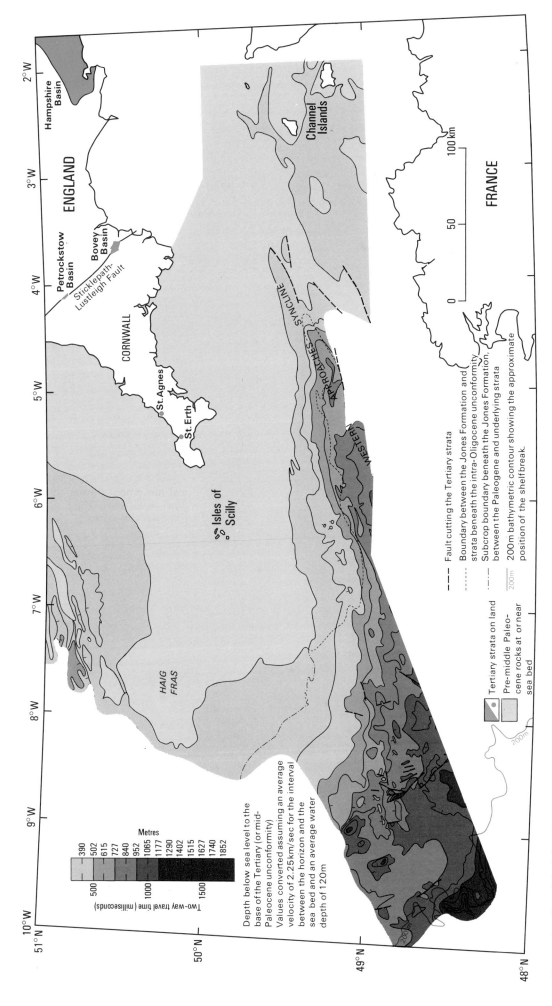

Figure 41 Simplified depth to the base of the Tertiary

9 Tertiary

The existence of Tertiary strata in the western English Channel was first confirmed early this century when nummulite-bearing sediments were dredged from the area (Crawshay, 1908; Worth, 1908; Dangeard, 1923 and 1929). Curry et al. (1971) later recognised Danian chalk and some Paleocene clays overlain by a thick succession of Eocene sand and limestone, and a few minor outcrops of Oligocene limestone. The sequence was overlain to the west by Miocene Globigerina Silts (Curry et al., 1965b) and a unit of possible Pliocene age with distinctive undulating seismic reflectors (Bouysse et al., 1975; Hamilton, 1979). Subsequent drilling and sampling has added substantial new information on the buried Tertiary sections. (Andreieff et al., 1975; BGS Solid Geology sheets).

The nearest extensive onshore Tertiary section to the report area is in the Hampshire Basin (Figure 4), which contains a late Thanetian to early Oligocene succession about 650 m thick (Melville and Freshney, 1982). These strata were folded and faulted by Alpine crustal movements; Melville and Freshney (1982) attribute a Miocene age to these movements, but there is little specific evidence from the basin or its surrounds for this assumption. This tectonic activity reached its peak offshore during the late Eocene to mid-Oligocene, when the whole area was uplifted. Localised subsidence along the Western Approaches syncline continued during the Miocene and renewed broad uplift affected the region during the late Miocene to Pliocene.

Chalk sedimentation continued across the continental shelf from the Late Cretaceous into the Danian, but by Thanetian times a global fall in sea level (Haq et al., 1987), coupled with minor tectonic activity, led to a regression recognised from the continental slope to the Hampshire Basin. From the late Paleocene to the late Eocene, the Western Approaches Trough was a shallow gulf opening westwards and southwards to the Atlantic Ocean and bounded to the north-east by the low-lying land of the Cornubian Platform. Sedimentation was interrupted during the earliest middle Eocene (Lutetian), and by the mid-Tertiary tectonic events (Ziegler, 1987a). After the latter erosional episode, a sequence of limestone and clay of predominantly Miocene age accumulated in a sea that may originally have extended close to, and possibly across, the present coast. Regional late Miocene to Pliocene warping and erosion has removed most of these deposits from the inner shelf.

Palaeogene strata crop out (Figure 3) at, or near, sea bed in the western English Channel on the flanks of the Neogene core to the east-north-east-trending Western Approaches syncline, and cover much of the coast off northern Brittany south of a line from Alderney to Ushant. Across the outer shelf, the Neogene succession covers the Palaeogene unconformably to dip gently oceanward and thicken rapidly over the outermost shelf and slope. Vigorous canyon cutting on the slope has removed much of this cover to expose Palaeogene and Mesozoic strata in the canyon walls. The continental slope subsided to bathyal depths during the Late Cretaceous, a process which had more or less ceased by the late Eocene (Montadert et al., 1979).

The base of the Tertiary (Figure 41) is essentially parallel to the base Upper Cretaceous. The base has a maximum depth of about 1000 m below sea level across the Melville Basin and rises eastwards to a depth of about 750 m south of the Isles of Scilly and some 250 m south of Plymouth Bay. The base generally has a smooth form, but tectonism in the Melville and South Celtic Sea basins, largely the result of salt movement, has given it a locally more complex surface.

Along the northern flank of the St Mary's Basin, the lower Tertiary strata are folded in an east-north-east-trending monoclinal structure. Dips to the south of up to 9° are recorded on the steep, narrow limb of the monocline, whereas farther north, where the Cretaceous and Tertiary rocks overstep the Cornubian Platform, dips rarely exceed 1° (BGS Scilly Solid Geology sheet). Near the eastern closure of the Western Approaches syncline, the Neogene strata are folded into a series of gentle, open structures parallel to the east-north-east axis of the main syncline.

The Brittany and Southwest Channel basins have a much reduced Tertiary cover due to erosion following their uplift during the Oligocene (Ziegler, 1987b). The Ouessant–Alderney fault zone, which separates the Brittany Basin from the St Mary's Basin to the north (Figure 29), was the focus of vertical movement during the mid-Tertiary. The cumulative downthrow along the fault zone during this time was to the north.

Along the northern flank of the Cornubian Platform and the southern part of the South Celtic Sea Basin, late Eocene to Oligocene lignitic sand rests directly on Chalk and basement. Across the western part of the basin, these strata are covered by thin Miocene calcarenites (Kamerling, 1979). In the Fastnet Basin, the oldest Tertiary strata are of Middle Eocene age and rest on Chalk, but nearer the shelf edge the Tertiary is thin and of Miocene age (Robinson et al., 1981).

PALEOCENE

In the offshore area, intra-Paleocene erosion has cut down into the Chalk, and Danian and upper Maastrichtian Chalk are preserved only in the central part of the western English Channel and across the outer shelf (Figure 8). The upper Maastrichtian to Danian sequence is 120 m thick south of Start Point (Curry et al., 1971) where it consists of pale grey to white, argillaceous, soft chalk containing dark grey flints, and grades up into a granular limestone. Foraminifera are abundant, and bryozoan and echinoderm fragments may be present (Andreieff et al, 1975). A single sample of grey, marine, sandy clay of Thanetian age has been recovered from the western English Channel (Andreieff and Lefort, 1972) where the unit is up to 30 m thick (Curry et al., 1978).

On the outer shelf, well 73/1-1 contains 28 m of Danian chalk with flints, overlain disconformably by early Thanetian clay; a further, longer hiatus is recognised between this clay and the overlying Ypresian clay. At DSDP site 548 on the Goban Spur slope, a minor unconformity is recognised between white chalk of early Danian age and the lithologically similar late Maastrichtian chalk, but the significant hiatus at this site was of approximately 4 million years duration, between the Danian and the Thanetian sediments (Poag et al., 1985).

In the Hampshire Basin, the basal Tertiary terrestrial clays and sands of the Reading Formation are of Thanetian age (Curry et al., 1978), and rest unconformably on an eroded and piped Chalk surface (Melville and Freshney, 1982). The major unconformity from the onshore area to the slope is thus placed between the Danian and Thanetian, with minor breaks in the underlying Paleocene succession that have been largely obliterated by downcutting associated with the later event. In most wells, the basal Tertiary above the Danian Chalk is of Eocene age, though in well 73/1-1 a thin, early Thanetian, grey, sandy clay lies below early Ypresian clays. Thanetian clays 25 m thick also occur in well 83/24-1, and a 24 m-thick Thanetian section of sandstone passing up into a siltstone is found in well 74/1-1,1A. The 109 m-thick Paleocene unit recorded in well 73/14-1 has a threefold subdivision; a basal chalky Danian section, a mid-Paleocene marl with thin limestones, and upper Paleocene claystone and limestone.

The abundance of planktonic foraminifera in the Danian of well 73/13-1 from the western Melville Basin indicates deposition under outer shelf, open-marine conditions. The overlying Thanetian clay was deposited under similar conditions, but the sandstones in adjacent wells record the incoming of shallow-marine conditions related to regional regression. This sand could not have come from the Western Approaches Trough, across which the Chalk cover was almost complete at this time; the source may have been the south-western part of the Fastnet Basin where erosion during the post-Maastrichtian to pre-middle Eocene cut down into the sandy Wealden sediments (Robinson et al., 1981).

The degree of downcutting associated with the mid-to late Paleocene erosional event in the Western Approaches Trough may be assessed by examining the age of the strata preserved immediately beneath the erosion surface (Figure 8). The erosion was least in the centre of the western English Channel and along the outer shelf, where Danian strata are preserved. Elsewhere, the erosion has cut down into the Maastrichtian or Campanian to remove up to 200 m of chalk, which is approximately the thickness of the Maastrichtian to Paleocene interval in wells 73/13-1 and 73/14-1. Seismic profiles show this erosional surface to be smooth and nearly parallel with the reflectors in the underlying Chalk, but cut by isolated valleys. The erosion may be related to a short-lived Thanetian eustatic regression (Haq et al., 1987), but there may be a tectonic element to this event, for in the Hampshire Basin the basal Reading Formation rests unconformably on folded Chalk as old as the Turonian (Melville and Freshney, 1982).

The magnitude of early Tertiary erosion of the Chalk covering the massif areas is unknown. Morton (1982) records Armorican, but no Cornubian-derived heavy minerals in the onshore Reading Formation. This might imply that the Chalk covered much of Cornubia but had been eroded off most of Armorica by the late Paleocene, or that drainage at this time ran to the west from Cornubia. Palaeogeographic reconstructions suggest that Cornubia was a low-lying area until the early to middle Eocene, when uplift of the massif and possibly the whole of the Hampshire Basin led to removal of the Chalk cover to expose Palaeozoic rocks (Morton, 1982).

EOCENE

During the late Paleocene and Eocene, the shallow-marine gulf in the Western Approaches was part of a sea that extended eastwards into the English Channel; sedimentation was closely controlled by the eustatic changes in sea level and minor tectonic warping. In the Paris and Hampshire basins, the late Thanetian transgression moved south-westwards, introducing cooler water from the North Sea (Pomerol, 1982) and bringing heavy minerals from the Scottish Highlands (Morton, 1982). The shallow seas in the English Channel were joined to the North Sea from the late Thanetian or early Ypresian until the early Lutetian, when the rising Weald–Artois anticlinal barrier closed the link. Terrestrial flora from the Hampshire Basin suggest that the Eocene climate was warm throughout the year and possibly similar to that of the tropical lowlands of present-day south-east Asia (Melville and Freshney, 1982).

In the Western Approaches Trough, the Eocene is represented by a predominantly claystone unit overlain by a limestone or sandstone. The sequence was deposited under shelf conditions, although a major regression at the end of the Ypresian separated the deposition of the two major lithological units. In the centre of the Western Approaches Trough, the Eocene succession is almost 600 m thick; seismic profiles show the unit thinning onto the southern flank of the Cornubian Platform where the Eocene to Oligocene is 157 m thick in well 83/24-1.

The lowermost Eocene unit in the Melville Basin is a claystone up to 120 m thick, dark olive-grey to brown, calcareous, glauconitic, and locally shaly or sandy. This unit is stratigraphically equivalent to the London Clay Formation of the Hampshire Basin, where it is about 100 m thick (Melville and Freshney, 1982). To the east and along the margins of the Melville Basin, intercalations of limestone are common within and at the base of the unit. The claystone grades upwards into a grey siltstone in wells 73/13-1 and 73/14-1, but to the west in well 72/10-1A (Figure 42) and to the east in 73/12-1A, the clay grades up into a sandstone. The sandy base of the clay in 73/13-1 represents a transgressive event and the lower part of the unit was deposited in open-marine, outer shelf conditions. Abundant coarse bioclastic debris with rare planktonic foraminifera near the top of the unit herald the regression that resulted in a disconformity, and sediments of latest Ypresian age are absent.

In the St Mary's Bay Basin, the base of the Eocene claystone unit of the in well 85/28-1 is an early Ypresian olive-grey, calcareous, glauconitic sandstone intercalated with hard fossiliferous chalk (Figure 42). This passes up into the predominant claystone, which is overlain by sandstone. The most easterly well in the basin (87/16-1) proved at least 59 m of Ypresian, white, bioclastic limestone with traces of sandstone resting on Danian chalk. The well data confirm the interpretation by Curry et al. (1970) of an early Tertiary hiatus in the western English Channel, where the earliest Tertiary sediments are Ypresian glauconitic sandstone and carbonates overlying Chalk, or locally Thanetian clay.

In the Western Approaches Trough, the basal Eocene claystone passes up into a glauconitic sandstone at a break in sedimentation which Bennet et al. (1985) equate in well 72/10-1A with the Ypresian–Lutetian boundary (Figure 42). The change in lithology occurs at the same stratigraphic level in well 73/1-1. This regional shallowing and increase in clastic sediments may be associated with an uplift pulse which brought coarser detritus into the Hampshire Basin (Morton, 1982). This pulse is of late Ypresian

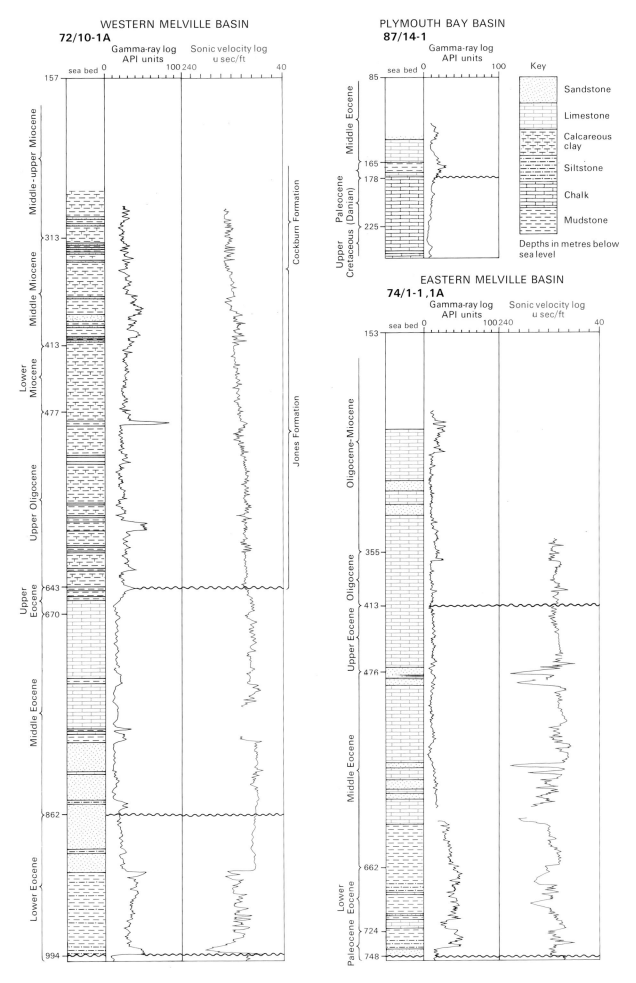

Figure 42 Simplified logs of Tertiary sections from wells in the Western Approaches Trough.

age, and is identified by the passage from the marine London Clay Formation up into the interdigitated marine and terrestrial sequences of the Bracklesham Group (Melville and Freshney, 1982).

In well 72/10-1A, the Lutetian sandstone is pale grey to yellowish grey, hard, glauconitic, fine grained, well sorted and cherty with a calcareous cement. This passes up into a pale greenish grey, granular, fine-grained, slightly glauconitic limestone with abundant bioclastic debris. This range of lithologies persists eastwards; in well 85/28-1 the sequence is predominantly sandy (Figure 42) and in the western English Channel (Curry et al., 1978) it is a calcareous sandstone. The first returns at the top of the succession in well 73/12-1A are of late Eocene age, and a number of other wells in the area record strata of the same age beneath the Oligocene unconformity (Figure 8). Hillis (1988) estimated that between 400 and 800 m of sediment was eroded from the area during the mid-Tertiary uplift and erosion (Figure 31). This value appears excessive considering the timespan of the hiatus and the typical rates of sedimentation through the Eocene.

During the Eocene, the shallow-marine gulf transgressed eastwards along the western English Channel. In this area Curry et al. (1978) report that early Eocene sediments have been recorded only west of about 6°W, and early middle Eocene beds west of 5°W. By the middle Eocene, the sea had transgressed onto the northern flanks of the Armorican Massif to deposit a broad sheet of sediment around the Channel Islands and north of Brittany. The oldest sediments in the area are of early Lutetian age, but late Lutetian and Bartonian sediments are also found (Andreieff et al. 1975). The Eocene in this part of the Channel consists of biosparite and biomicrite, locally silty and containing glauconite. The samples are composed largely of foraminiferal, bryozoan and echinoid fragments; calcareous algae and molluscan debris are also found. Faunal evidence suggests that the carbonates were laid down in warm, shallow water with local hypersaline lagoons. During the Eocene the western English Channel received little detrital sediment, most of the sediment coming from biogenic production. The lack of sediment resulted in shallow, clear water in which seagrass flourished. Salinities in the area reached 38‰ and the summer water temperatures exceeded 22°C (Murray and Wright, 1974). The contemporaneous Eocene sediments exposed on the northen limb of the Western Approaches Trough are more arenaceous, indicating that by the middle Eocene, Cornubia had attained a greater relief than Armorica (Morton, 1982).

Confirmation of the arenaceous nature of the upper unit on the northern limb of the Western Approaches Trough comes from a number of shallow BGS boreholes. Borehole 81/4 in the St Mary's Basin (Figure 7) drilled 47 m of finely interbedded, olive-grey, fine-grained sand and brown clay in beds generally less than a centimetre thick with irregular, bioturbated surfaces that are locally fractured by desiccation cracks. At 30 m below sea bed there is a thin band of rubbly, glauconitic limestone with cemented pebbles. The sequence ranges in age from late Ypresian to early Lutetian, and is of shallow-marine facies, with the desiccation cracks suggesting an intertidal environment.

Nearby borehole 79/2 was drilled about 150 m higher in the succession and recovered Lutetian to Bartonian shallow-marine, glauconitic, calcareous sand with limestone bands up to 10 cm thick. These are the youngest dated Eocene strata proved beneath the mid-Tertiary erosion surface, although seismic evidence indicates an additional 80 m of strata between the top of the borehole and the base of the overlying Miocene. The section immediately beneath the Miocene was penetrated in borehole 81/9, where it consists of skeletal, bioclastic limestone rich in bryozoan and molluscan debris. Powell (1988) suggests an Oligocene or older age for the limestone based on the impoverished dinoflagellate cyst assemblage.

OLIGOCENE

The Oligocene was a period of great tectonic upheaval across the region. During much of this epoch, large areas of the continental shelf were subjected to a series of erosional events that had started during the latest Eocene. Across the northern basins of the Western Approaches Trough the erosion stripped away any lower Oligocene strata to cut down into the underlying Eocene and Paleocene and, on the northern flanks of the trough, into the Chalk. The magnitude of the tectonic uplift that caused the erosion was greatest across the Brittany Basin, and generally decreased westwards to fade out over the Bay of Biscay continental slope (Ziegler, 1987b). Almost all of the eroded material was probably transported over the shelf edge, for there are no extensive Oligocene deposits in the Western Approaches Trough.

Determination of the late Eocene to late Oligocene stratigraphy and palaeogeography of the area is hampered by the limited thickness and geographical extent of the preserved sequences (Figure 8). In the Hampshire Basin, the predominantly shallow-marine conditions changed during the late middle Eocene to the fluvial and lagoonal facies which persisted into the early Oligocene, the age of the youngest strata preserved onshore in this basin. There was also at this time a significant cooling of the previously warm climate (Melville and Freshney, 1982). Minor outcrops of similar facies, and of Oligocene age, have been proved in the western English Channel. Sediments of early Oligocene age have been proved in the Western Approaches Trough to the west, but in this area they lie above the regional unconformity and extend upwards as an unbroken sequence into the Miocene.

An extensive sequence of upper Eocene to lower Oligocene shallow-marine sand overlies unconformably the Chalk and basement on the northern margin of the Cornubian Platform and the adjoining South Celtic Sea Basin. A very thick but localised Eocene to Oligocene sequence occurs within the pull apart basins developed both onshore and offshore along the Sticklepath–Lustleigh Fault. The tectonic setting and age range of the sediments within these basins are important evidence in the unravelling of the tectonic history of the region during Tertiary time. The preserved mid-Tertiary sequences offshore demonstrate that although horizontal movement along this fault spanned the late Eocene and Oligocene, the response of the crust under the offshore basins to these stresses was neither synchronous nor of the same magnitude across the region.

The Alpine stresses that led to the regional uplift, combined with the changes in the pattern of sea-floor spreading at the Mid-Atlantic Ridge, led to the intrusion of olivine-dolerite dykes in south-west Ireland during the late Eocene and late Oligocene (Horne and Macintyre, 1975). A north-north-west-trending dyke swarm of late Oligocene age also occurs to the south-west of Ireland (Seemann, 1984). Farther south, in the Fastnet Basin, a plug deforms reflections up to the top of the Chalk, and may be of the same age as the dykes described above (Caston et al., 1981).

While the continental shelf was being uplifted and eroded, the slope also suffered a period of nondeposition or erosion. A hiatus, of approximately 4 million years duration, is recorded between the early and late Oligocene nannofossil chalk at site 548 on the Goban Spur slope (Poag et al., 1985; Snyder et al., 1985). This hiatus is widely recorded on the continental slopes of the North Atlantic and has been attributed to the erosive effects of along-slope currents during a time when ocean circulation was more vigorous than at present. Seismic profiles suggest erosional retreat of the Western Approaches slope during this time, and the formation of canyons that were subsequently infilled.

The pre-unconformity Oligocene sequence

In the Hampshire Basin, a transition from dominantly marine to freshwater sediments occurred during the Bartonian; these conditions persisted into the Rupelian when the clay, loam, sand and shale of the Bouldnor Formation were deposited (Edwards and Freshney, 1987). No younger Tertiary strata are preserved in the basin and the main tectonic uplift and localised folding of the area therefore postdates the early Oligocene, though the change in facies may have signalled the start of the event. The only evidence for early Oligocene sediments in the Western Approaches Trough under the regional unconformity are the small outliers that crop out to the south-west of the Hurd Deep (Figure 3). Two facies have been recognised by Andreieff and Lefort (1972): a green clay with a limited brackish-water microfauna which compares with the Bouldnor Formation in the Isle of Wight, and biocalcarenites with a rich marine microfauna typical of the early Oligocene in the Aquitaine Basin. A buff limestone with moulds of freshwater gastropods typical of the Bouldnor Formation was also found in the area resting disconformably on late Eocene sands (Curry et al., 1978). The lithological similarity of these outliers with contemporaneous units exposed on both sides of the Channel suggested to Pomerol (1982) that deposition occurred during the late Eocene to early Oligocene in a seaway through the western English Channel into a restricted Paris Basin.

There is a widespread hiatus on the middle and outer shelf between the late or middle Eocene beds and the earliest Oligocene sediment, the oldest of which is the middle Rupelian claystone overlying middle Lutetian sandstone in well 73/1-1. Thus the tectonic activity which caused the unconformity had more or less finished by the mid-early Oligocene in the western part of the Melville Basin, but had barely commenced at this time farther east in the western English Channel and Hampshire Basin.

The post-unconformity Oligocene sequence in the northern part of the Western Approaches Trough

The Oligocene to Miocene Jones and Cockburn formations are disposed as an oceanward-dipping and thickening wedge preserved from the middle shelf south-westwards onto the slope. The only significant departure from this geometry is the increase in thickness of the unit towards the core of the Western Approaches syncline south of the Isles of Scilly (Figure 43) due to subsidence along the trough axis during the early Miocene (Evans and Hughes, 1984). This subsidence was probably related to continued northerly downthrow on the Ouessant–Alderney fault zone at this time. The basal Jones Formation transgression advanced eastwards across the outer shelf and into the western English Channel. The oldest, Oligocene, part of the unit is therefore restricted to the outer shelf and deeply buried, whereas to the east, the youngest part of the unit exposed at sea bed is of early Miocene age.

The oldest Oligocene strata recovered above the regional unconformity are the 37 m of pale green, glauconitic, middle Rupelian claystone in well 73/1-1. The claystone is overlain by at least 100 m of fine-grained, white, Chattian sandstone grading into a soft, clayey limestone. A similar sandstone occurs at the base of the unit in well 73/4-1 farther east. The Chattian section is 166 m thick in well 72/10-1A and consists of yellowish grey, marly chalk with brownish grey chert fragments and silt-sized glauconite grains (Figure 42). The bulk of the sequence was deposited in open-marine, outer shelf conditions with an influx of humic kerogen on the lower part suggesting an initial, shallower, inner shelf environment.

The concentration of hydrocarbon wells near salt swells may distort and exaggerate the regional stratigraphic range of the hiatus as compared to that developed away from salt swells. Seismic profiles show upper Palaeogene strata onlapping the flanks of the uplifts caused by salt swells (Figure 32), though both onlap and the rise of the salt wall had almost ceased by the time the post-unconformity units were being deposited.

The post-unconformity late Eocene to early Oligocene sequence north of the Cornubian Platform

Erosion removed any Tertiary strata of pre-late Eocene age that had been deposited on the northern flanks of the Cornubian Platform and South Celtic Sea Basin. A broad expanse of upper Eocene to Oligocene sediments now rests with marked unconformity on an eroded, largely Chalk or basement surface across this area (Figure 3). On seismic profiles, the unit displays subparallel to parallel reflectors of varied continuity and amplitude. Low-angled channels of variable size and shape, infilled with more confused reflectors, cut the near horizontal reflectors.

Over the very flat northern flank of the Cornubian Platform, the unit overlies the Chalk, is nearly horizontal, and has a maximum thickness of about 100 m. On the southern margin of the South Celtic Sea Basin, the unit is caught up in a series of structures related to the underlying salt swells and is over 300 m thick in the axis of some synclines (Figure 41). The disconformably overlying Miocene strata to the north-west of the Haig Fras inlier (Figure 3) are not folded to the same extent as the Oligocene unit, indicating that salt movement had largely stopped in this area by the end of the Oligocene.

In the South Celtic Sea Basin, the Chalk in well 93/2-1 is overlain unconformably by a 106 m-thick unit of dark greenish grey, noncalcareous mudstone or siltstone, and medium-to coarse-grained sand, alternating with beds of dark brown to black lignite. The sequence in well 93/6-1 is lithologically similar except that white sandstone predominates. In borehole 81/7 (Figure 7), the unit has a silicified basal conglomerate less than a metre thick resting on soft Maastrichtian Chalk. Samples from borehole 79/3 (Figure 7) were devoid of calcareous microfauna, and the occurrence of microgranular pyrite may indicate a reducing environment in which the calcareous fauna was dissolved. Borehole 79/3 contains a poor dinoflagellate cyst association, but is rich in pollen and terrigenous material. Similar results have been obtained from nearby sea-bed samples, and the biostratigraphic evidence suggests a late Eocene to early Oligocene age for the unit which was deposited in a nearshore environment on a very shallow shelf traversed by a channel system.

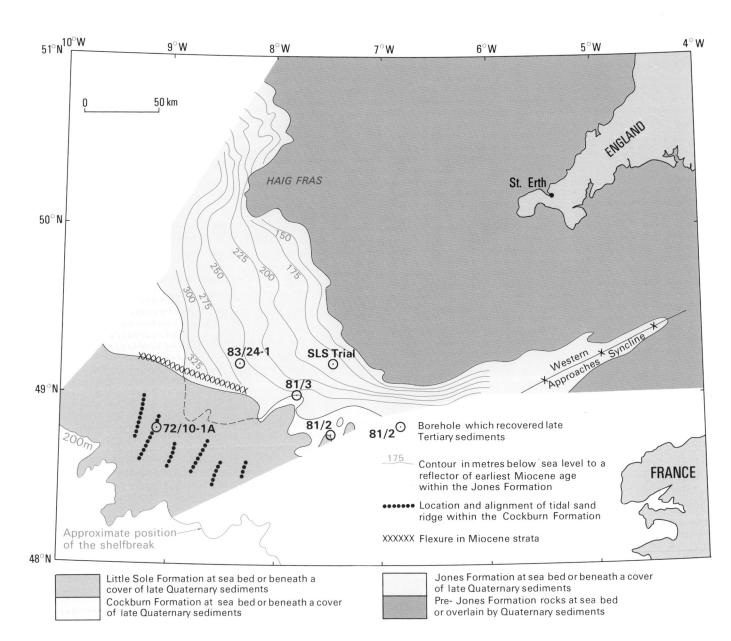

Figure 43 The geometry of the Neogene units

There is no indication that the present southern edge of the Oligocene is close to its original limit. Walsh et al. (1987) describe very small outliers of Oligocene age from south Cornwall at an altitude of about 120 m above OD which show some palynological and lithological similarities with the Bovey Formation, and were deposited in a frost-free, nonmarine, low-energy, possibly lacustrine environment.

Bovey Formation

The Bovey, Petrockstow (Figure 41) and Stanley Bank pull-apart basins are developed along the Sticklepath-Lustleigh Fault. This fault is one of a set of north-north-westerly trending wrench faults traversing the South-West Peninsula (Dearman, 1963), but is the only one to have suffered substantial movement during the Tertiary and to have narrow, deep basins of this age developed along its length.

The largest basin, the Bovey Basin, contains a sequence estimated to be over 1200 m thick, although only 300 m have been proved by drilling (Edwards, 1976; Selwood et al., 1984). The infilling Bovey Formation consists of clay with sandy intercalations and lignite which have been dated from plant remains as Oligocene or possibly Miocene

at the top, passing down into early Oligocene with Eocene indications below 290 m (Selwood et al., 1984). Deposition took place in river flood plains where sedimentation kept pace with subsidence.

There is no evidence from offshore that deposition of the Oligocene strata on the northern margin of the Cornubian Platform was controlled by this set of wrench faults, except north of the report where the Stanley Bank Basin, to the east of Lundy Island, lies alongside the offshore extension of the Sticklepath–Lustleigh Fault (Fletcher, 1975). The age range of the sediments in these basins is evidence that the tectonic episode which led to the regional Tertiary unconformity stretched at least from the late Eocene through the Oligocene and possibly into the Miocene (Selwood et al., 1984). An earth tremor in 1955 indicates that movement on the fault continues to the present (Dearman, 1963).

NEOGENE

The northern part of the Western Approaches Trough became tectonically less active after the upheaval of mid-Tertiary uplift and erosion. A rise in eustatic sea level which commenced during the early Chattian (Haq et al., 1987) continued with minor fluctuations into the early Serravallian (middle Miocene). The transgression related to this sea level rise led to deposition of a sequence of marine calcareous clastic sediments, commencing in the middle Rupelian on the outer shelf and encroaching onto the middle shelf in the Miocene. This transgression covered much of north-western France at its maximum, but did not extend into the Paris Basin or the eastern English Channel (Pomerol, 1982). Late Neogene tilting followed by shelf-wide erosion has removed the Neogene sediments from the inner shelf where they are now preserved only in the axis of the Western Approaches syncline (Figure 43).

The original extent of Miocene marine sediments across southern Britain is uncertain. The only remnants of Neogene strata preserved in south-west England (Figure 41) are the Miocene wind-blown and colluvial sands at St Agnes (Walsh et al., 1987), and the late Pliocene shallow marine sand and clay at St Erth (Houghton and Jenkins 1988; Maybury and Whatley, 1986). A peneplanation surface in the region at an elevation of up to 330 m above OD has been attributed to Miocene marine erosion (Edmonds et al., 1975). However, Walsh et al. (1987) suggest that the gross onshore physiography was established by the Oligocene, and that the region has not been subsequently covered by a major marine transgression. The Bovey Formation is mostly of Eocene to Oligocene age, but Chandler (1964) considered from plant evidence that the formation might range into the Miocene.

By contrast, the Miocene transgression extended across much of north-west France to deposit coarse shelly sand with a rich, tropical fauna. A late Miocene regression was followed by renewed deposition of Pliocene shelly marl that on the flanks of the Brittany Peninsula is overlain by, or is laterally equivalent to, a sequence of shelly sand similar to the Coralline Crag of East Anglia (Pomerol, 1982).

On the Goban Spur continental slope, an almost complete late Oligocene to Recent succession of calcareous nannofossil ooze with turbiditic silt was recovered from site 548. The only break recognised in the 352 m-thick succession is a hiatus of late Serravallian to early Tortonian age (Poag et al., 1985) which coincided with an eustatic fall in sea level brought about by increased global ice volumes, and resulted in enhanced current activity in the water masses impinging on the slope (Poag et al., 1985). Late Tertiary and Pleistocene canyon cutting and slope wasting has removed much of the Neogene sediment deposited on the Western Approaches slope; only one of the three DSDP boreholes drilled on this slope recovered Miocene sediments, and at this site there was a hiatus between the deposition of early Miocene chalk and late Pliocene ooze (Montadert et al., 1979).

Evans and Hughes (1984) divide the shelf sequence above the Oligocene unconformity and beneath the glacially related Quaternary strata into three formations (Figure 43). The oldest, the Jones Formation, extends into the Langhian, and is truncated by erosion on the middle shelf. This formation is equivalent to the 'Globigerina Silts' of Curry et al. (1962). The top of the overlying Cockburn Formation is a shelf-wide erosion surface of possible late Miocene age (Figure 45). The uppermost division, the Little Sole Formation, is divided into a lower, lens-shaped unit confined largely to the upper continental slope, and an upper, blanket-like unit covering the outer shelf. This formation has not been extensively sampled and its age range is not known, but the youngest

sediments within it are probably contemporaneous with the St Erth Beds onshore.

Jones Formation

The Jones Formation underlies the outer shelf (Figure 43), where it rests on the gently oceanward-dipping surface of the Oligocene unconformity. The base of the formation transgressed eastwards and northwards into the Western Approaches Trough and across the Cornubian Platform to overstep Eocene and Cretaceous sediments as well as Devonian to Carboniferous strata west of the Haig Fras inlier. It was named the Globigerina Silts by Curry et al. (1962) and ascribed a Pliocene age, but later re-examination (Curry et al., 1965b) placed the silts in the Miocene. Evans and Hughes (1984) date the formation from BGS boreholes drilled across the northern part of the St Mary's Basin as Aquitanian to Langhian, but on the outer shelf in well 73/1-1 its base is of middle Rupelian age, and in well 72/10-1A it is of Chattian age. In the latter well the top of the Jones Formation is possibly of early Serravallian age. Powell (1988) examined the dinoflagellate cyst assemblege from the BGS boreholes and favoured a late Aquitanian to middle Serravallian age for the sequences.

The basal erosion surface beneath the Jones Formation is usually smooth, though a more rugged, palaeokarst relief with an amplitude measured in tens of metres occurs where the unit overlies Eocene limestone (Evans and Hughes, 1984). The formation was deposited in a shelf sea slightly deeper and warmer than presently found in the area (Jenkins and Shackleton, 1979; Jenkins, 1977), with limited terrestrial input and tranquil sea-bed conditions. At its maximum, the Jones Formation probably covered most of the continental shelf of the region, but may not have encroached onto southern Britain (Walsh et al., 1987).

The reflectors at the base of the formation are a series of low-angled south-westerly-dipping clinoforms that pass up into parallel, continuous reflectors traceable over thousands of square kilometres (Figure 44). The formation is 294 m thick in well 72/10-1A, but thins to about half this value eastwards across the middle shelf (Figure 42) where it is an olive-grey, intensely bioturbated, silty calcilutite with thin, slightly coarser beds. The sediments are rich in benthonic and planktonic foraminifera, ostracods, and debris from echinoderms and molluscs. Radiolaria are common and triradiate sponge spicules occur in the lower part of the sequence. The heavy minerals are distinctly Cornubian in origin and dominated by tourmaline. The basal metre of the formation in borehole 81/9 is rich in coarse mica flakes and rounded phosphate pebbles (Evans and Hughes, 1984).

Cockburn Formation

Across the middle shelf, the continuity and parallelism of the reflectors of the Jones Formation are terminated at an erosion surface where there is an abrupt change in seismic reflector characteristics (Figure 45). Below the erosion surface, the reflectors in the upper part of the Jones Formation are nearly horizontal and parallel, but above, the Cockburn Formation displays downlapping reflectors or forms a series of low undulating banks with an inclined infill of the intervening lows. Along the northern margin of the St Mary's Basin, erosion has removed up to 120 m of the Jones Formation, but the magnitude of this erosion decreases to the south-west. Across much of the outer

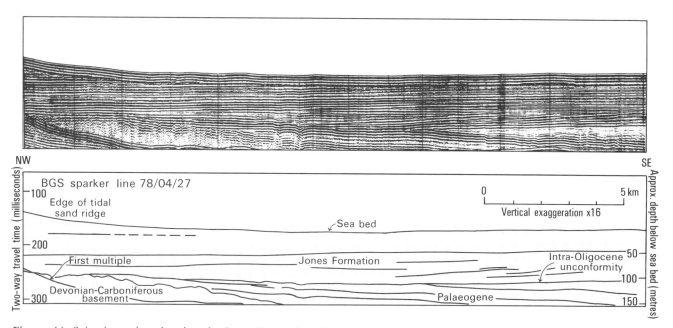

Figure 44 Seismic section showing the Jones Formation. For location see Figure 6.

shelf, the boundary between the Jones and Cockburn formations is a disconformity recognised only by a subtle change in reflector character.

The formation was drilled in borehole 81/2 where it is lithologically similar to the underlying Jones Formation except that it is a slightly coarser, silty calcarenite with a higher proportion of heavy minerals of Scottish Highland derivation. The basal sediments have a Serravallian age and the youngest part of the unit drilled in well 72/10-1A is dated as late Serravallian to early Tortonian (Bennet et al., 1985; Evans and Hughes, 1984). The poor dinoflagellate assemblages from the formation in the BGS boreholes reported on by Evans and Hughes (1984) were given a possible late Tortonian to Pleistocene age by Powell (1988), but regional seismic interpretation suggests that these dates may be spurious.

Reflectors in the basal part of the formation form low banks (tidal sand ridges) up to 60 m high and 6 to 8 km across, orientated in a north-north-easterly direction with a spacing of 12 to 20 km (Figure 43). The banks are smooth in profile, generally symmetrical, and have a complex internal reflector geometry. The reflectors between the banks form a series of low-angled, dish-like infills which decrease in amplitude upwards. The banks are similar in geometry and size to those on the present sea bed in the area (Figure 11); these (see p. 00) are the product of strong tidal currents during the late Devensian–early Flandrian when sea level was lower than at present (Pantin and Evans, 1984). The appearance of the banks in the Cockburn Formation, without a significant change in the lithology from that of the Jones Formation, is probably related to a lowering of sea level across the area.

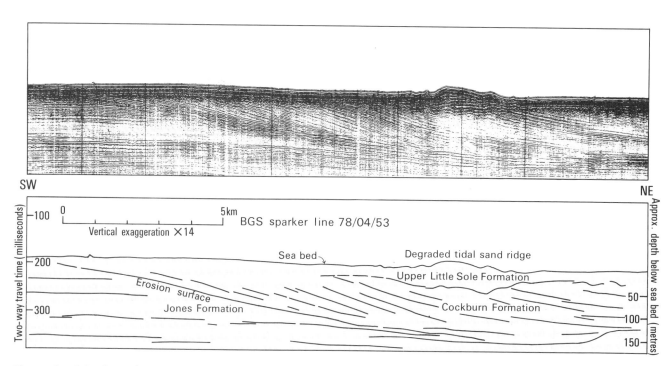

Figure 45 Seismic section showing the erosion surface at the base of the Cockburn Formation. For location see Figure 6.

Little Sole Formation

The depositional style and geometry of the Little Sole Formation is very different from that of the underlying formations, reflecting a major change in the depositional regime on the shelf and upper slope. The cessation of the shelf-wide, carbonate-rich deposition of the Cockburn Formation may correlate with the late Miocene to early Pliocene regression recognised in north-west France, and a global eustatic fall in sea level (Haq et al., 1987). On the Goban Spur, deposition restarted during the Tortonian after a short hiatus, and the oldest part of the Little Sole Formation on the slope may be of approximately the same age.

The Little Sole Formation is informally divided into two units. The lower is a lens-like body with an uniform along-slope form (Figure 14), resting unconformably on the upper slope and the outermost shelf (Figure 43). The upper, blanket-like unit covers much of the outer shelf and drapes onto the slope. A disconformity separates the two units on the outer shelf, but on the slope they are seismically indistinguishable and appear conformable.

Lower Little Sole Formation

Erosion of the shelf and slope during the late Miocene regression was followed by deposition of the lower Little Sole unit, when abundant sediment accumulated onto the prograding outermost shelf and upper slope. This sediment influx may have been derived from the tilting and subsequent erosion of the inner shelf which truncated the Miocene units and produced a series of cliffs and submerged terraces around the present coast (Page 00 and Figure 10).

The lower Little Sole Formation has a maximum thickness of 300 m slightly oceanward of the shelfbreak. Its base under the outer shelf is a slightly undulating unconformity which extends with a dip of about 3° from a water depth of about 250 m to at least 1700 m (Figure 14); below 1200 m it is nearly parallel to the depositional dip of the underlying strata. The basal erosion surface rises upslope onto the outer continental shelf to flatten out about 15 km landward of the shelfbreak and continue to the north-east at about 50 to 60 m below the present sea bed (Evans and Hughes, 1984). The basal surface of the formation has an irregular, undulating, along-slope form, suggesting that the upper slope was incised by a series of canyons prior to deposition of the unit.

Pleistocene erosion on the upper slope has produced a mass of interlocking canyons and slump zones that have cut into and removed much of the lower Little Sole Formation. Only along the rare, smoothly sloping interfluves between the canyons is the unit not eroded. A complete section of the lens extends south-westwards from about 48°2′N 9°25′W where there is a smooth transition from the outer shelf onto the upper slope (Figure 12e). On the shelf, the lower part of the unit contains a series of prograding units within its usually chaotic reflector pattern. Below a water depth of about 350 m, this signature passes rapidly into a more continuous, high-amplitude pattern in which the reflectors are generally parallel but contain slump lenses and listric fault planes, especially near the base.

Seismic profiles run along the upper slope show that the lens was originally a more continuous feature with a surface form simpler than at present. In Figure 14, the rugged incised upper slope is the result of backwall erosion from an off-line canyon, and the smooth original form of the formation surface prior to canyon cutting is easily visualised (see also Figure·12b). Late Miocene to Pliocene and Pleistocene canyon-related erosion is absent from the gently inclined Goban Spur continental slope, but extensive erosion occurred during these times on the steeper Western Approaches slope.

Upper Little Sole Formation

This blanket-like unit, about 50 m thick, displays a chaotic, very discontinuous, variable amplitude reflector character. Channels, a few tens of metres deep and a few hundred metres across, are traced along the shelf at the base of the unit, and extend down to a depth of 240 m below sea level near the shelf edge (Bouysse et al., 1975; 1976). The channel axes are almost straight, traceable over distances in excess of 100 km, and aligned at a slightly oblique angle to the dip of the present shelf. They generally deepen oceanwards, though some show a deepening towards the north-north-east. These characteristics of the channel thalweg led Bouysse et al. (1975) to infer that the shelf had been tilted since their incision. The channels do not lead directly into canyon heads, though subsequent slumping and canyon-head erosion may have removed the link between the two. Farther south, to the west of the Brittany Peninsula, river channels are known to cross the shelf and link with canyon heads (Pinot, 1974).

The only sample recovered from this part of the formation on the outer shelf is an early Pleistocene, olive-grey, clayey sand (Evans and Hughes, 1984), although Curry et al. (1965b) described a sample of similar age and lithology collected about 100 km south of Land's End. Both samples indicate deposition in water depths greater than about 50 m and may be part of the same depositional unit as the late Pliocene St Erth Beds (see below) in western Cornwall (Jenkins, 1982).

The continuous sheet on the outer shelf terminates abruptly to the north-north-east at a possible flexured contact where the base of the unit steepens in dip to crop out at sea bed (Figure 43). Reflectors in the underlying Neogene sediments display a flexure down to the west directly under this zone, demonstrating that the present limit of the unit is structurally controlled.

St Erth Beds

A small outlier of Pliocene sand and clay is preserved resting on an eroded surface of Devonian slate at St Erth on the south-eastern slopes of the Hayle valley in Cornwall (Figure 41). The deposits, named the St Erth Beds, are at a height of between 30 and 37 m above OD, and have a maximum thickness of about 7 m. They consist of a basal unit of yellow, fine-grained, clayey sand overlain by blue or yellow, weathered clay and soliflucted sand, clay and broken rock.

The extensive macrofauna of the beds led early workers to propose a Pliocene age for the deposit, and a correlation with the Coralline Crag and Red Crag of Suffolk. Planktonic foraminiferal studies (Jenkins, 1982; Jenkins et al., 1986) place the beds in the late Pliocene between 1.9 and 2.1 Ma. Extensive palaeoecological work (Maybury and Whatley, 1986; Houghton and Jenkins, 1988) indicates that the beds were laid down in a warm, shallow (<10 m) sea with temperatures similar to those of the present Mediterranean.

During the deposition of the St Erth beds, the sea extended from south Cornwall to northern France, and may have formed a shallow gulf in the Hayle area where sea level was at an altitude of about 45 to 50 m above OD. The rise in sea level to this altitude left no discernible bevel in the landscape and represented the only time during the middle to late Tertiary when the sea encroached onto the present land area of the Cornubian Massif (Walsh et al., 1987).

10 Quaternary

Across most of the continental shelf of the report area there is a stratigraphic break between the Tertiary/early Pleistocene and the later Pleistocene/Holocene sediments. There is no evidence to suggest that the region was a depocentre similar to the North Sea during the Quaternary (Cameron et al., 1987), and any sediments laid down during the hiatus were probably removed during low stands related to the late Pleistocene glaciations.

The area lay at the southernmost margin of the great Pleistocene ice sheets, the precise extents of which are in dispute, for the evidence is limited. The nearest substantial glacial Pleistocene succession is found in the Celtic Deep of the north Celtic Sea; the southern feather edge of this deposit extends into the northernmost part of the area and possibly south-westwards to the west of Haig Fras (Figure 9). On the outer shelf, to the south of this limit, there are isolated mounds of glacial debris at the sea bed; till is found on the Isles of Scilly, and some erratics have been recovered from the floor and margins of the English Channel. The ice sheets pressed against, but may not have surmounted, the cliffs forming the northern coast of south-west England (Mitchell and Orme, 1967) to leave isolated, tantalising evidence of their former existence. These lines of evidence have led to proposals that a glaciation of Wolstonian (Saalian) age (Figure 46) extended as far south as the Isles of Scilly (Mitchell and Orme, 1967), or covered the whole of the western English Channel and much of the Western Approaches (Kellaway et al., 1975). Alternatively, a tongue of the last major Devensian ice sheet occupied some of these areas (Scourse, in press; Wingfield, 1990).

The Quaternary (Pleistocene and Holocene) sequences display a great variation in their preserved geometries. On the Goban Spur continental slope, a complete bathyal Pliocene and Pleistocene sequence was recovered at DSDP site 548 (de Graciansky and Poag, 1985). A similar sequence is probably preserved to the south in the canyon interfluves on the Western Approaches and Bay of Biscay slopes. In contrast, the bulk of the preserved Quaternary sequence on the continental shelf was deposited in a short

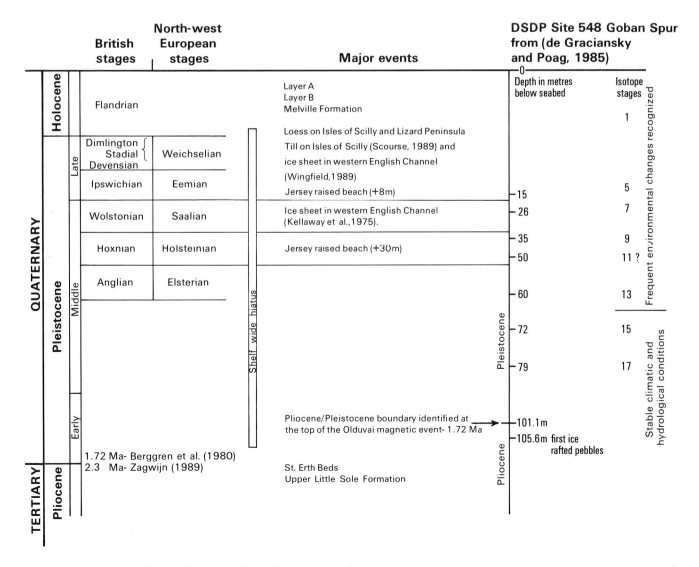

Figure 46 Stratigraphic relationships of the Quaternary units

period during the later part of the last glacial event, the Dimlington Stadial (Rose, 1985), and later reworked by the late Devensian–Flandrian transgression. However, in the Hurd Deep and at the southern end of the Celtic Deep, thicker and more complex Quaternary sections are preserved. All these sequences (except for site 548) are poorly sampled and have not been correlated either with each other or with the successions preserved on the adjoining land. There is no evidence to suggest that the present limited thickness of Quaternary sediments on the shelf is due to significant glacial or marine erosion, though the smoothness of the planation surface that truncates the Pleistocene units at the southern flank of the Celtic Deep Quaternary basin testifies to the erosive efficiency of the postglacial transgression.

Pantin and Evans (1984) divided the Quaternary strata in the southern and western parts of the continental shelf into four units: (1) The oldest, the upper Little Sole Formation, a Pliocene to early Pleistocene sheet-like unit restricted to the outer shelf, (2) the Melville Formation, which comprises the bulk of the tidal sand ridges and some intervening lows, (3) Layer B, a sandy, gravelly lag pavement forming a thin sheet across the top of the underlying units, and (4) Layer A, the partly mobile sediment at the sea bed. Figure 46 shows the stratigraphic relationship between these Quaternary units.

During the Dimlington Stadial, the main glacial episode during the late Devensian which spanned approximately 26 000 to 13 000 years BP, sea level in the Celtic Sea fell to about 120 to 135 m below its present level (Bouysse et al., 1976) to expose the inner and middle shelf. The recognition of old cliff lines at – 205 m off the Brittany coast (Pinot, 1974), and the depth of the shelf-break at the Western Approaches margin at between – 180 and – 205 m suggest that the fall in sea level may have been even greater during an earlier Pleistocene glacial episode. However, the area may have subsided since that earlier planation event. The Dimlington Stadial was the last of a number of episodes during the Pleistocene when the shelf was subjected to erosion. During the succeeding late Devensian–Flandrian transgression, the high energy littoral zone migrated landward across the shelf over sediments deposited as an outwash plain during the preceeding glacial period to leave Layer B winnowed out at its top. The subsequent rise in sea level and decrease in terrigenous sediment input, combined with an increase in bioclastic input, led to the deposition of the Layer A mobile sediments. These were subjected to rapidly changing hydraulic conditions, and readjustment of layers A and B is still in progress with sand in transit westwards across the shelf (Stride, 1963).

ONSHORE OCCURRENCES

Most of Devon and Cornwall remained ice free during the glacial periods, but there is evidence from a number of coastal sites that at least one ice sheet extended this far south (Stephens, 1970; 1973). Deposits at these sites have proved difficult to date, and most correlations of the Quaternary deposits and geomorphological features are tentative.

The most intriguing onshore Quaternary deposits in the region are preserved on the northern islands of the Isles of Scilly. Barrow (1906) described the type-site from Chad Girt on White Island (Figure 9), near St Martin's, where deeply weathered granite bedrock is overlain by a solifluicted head deposit, lodgement till derived from the

north, and outwash gravels. Raised beach deposits occur both above and below the glacial sediments. Mitchell and Orme (1967) considered the glacial deposits to be of Wolstonian (Saalian) age, but the solifluicted material overlying the lower raised beach, and predating the glacial advance, yielded C[14] ages between 34 500 and 21 500 years BP. It also contains a pollen assemblage similar to sediments of this age from elsewhere in north-west Europe (Scourse, 1985; in press). Further evidence for the age of the glaciation comes from the loess which covers much of the islands (Catt and Staines, 1982); on the southern islands of St Agnes and St Mary's this coarse aeolian silt yielded two thermoluminescence dates of 18 600 years BP (Wintle, 1981). This loess may be associated with an ice advance across the northern Isles of Scilly, or the continental shelf immediately to the north, during the Dimlington Stadial. The lower raised beach sequence on White Island also contains erratic material indicating that an earlier (pre-late Devensian) glaciation may have covered part of the islands (Scourse, in press).

There are other limited occurrences of glacial deposits along the coast of Devon and Cornwall (Stephens, 1970; Mitchell et al., 1973). Around the margins of Barnstaple Bay immediately north of the report area (Figure 1), large erratics associated with head rest on a series of wave-cut platforms, and a boulder clay sequence is preserved nearby at Fremington. To the south, at Trebetherick Point (Figure 9) a series of bedded outwash gravels containing erratics rest on rock platforms. Other erratic blocks resting on wave-cut platforms along the coast include the garnet-iferous microcline gneiss at Porthleven (Figure 9), but this may originate from the local basement (Exley, 1987; Goode and Merriman, 1987) rather than the Highlands of Scotland derivation proposed by Flett and Hill (1946).

The loess of the Isles of Scilly is also recognised on the Lizard where it forms a mottled yellow-brown silt up to 0.9 m thick both on the plateau surface of the peninsula and on solifluction terraces (Roberts, 1985). The loess here has yielded an age of 15 900 years BP (Wintle, 1981), and may have been derived from the vast outwash plain that was exposed on the continental shelf to the north-north-west at this time (Catt and Staines, 1982), although evidence from similar deposits on the Channel Islands suggests an easterly source (Keen, 1978). There is no evidence for ice encroaching onto the Channel Islands, where three raised beach sequences are recognised (Keen, 1978 and Figure 46).

Kellaway et al. (1975) advanced the controversial view that the English Channel and the shelf had been covered by one or more Quaternary ice sheets. They proposed that the ice sheet during the Dimlington Stadial terminated along the southern coast of Wales, but that ice sheets had extended eastwards into the English Channel and westwards across the continental shelf to the shelfbreak during the Wolstonian (Saalian) to leave parts of southern England uncovered.

THE QUATERNARY SUCCESSION ON THE UPPER SLOPE

During the Pliocene to Pleistocene, sedimentation was almost continuous on parts of the continental slope, with none of the erosion which interrupted the shallower water and terrestrial sequences. However, such are the lithological and faunal differences between the two environments that correlation between them remains tenuous. An almost complete Pliocene to Pleistocene succession of largely fossiliferous ooze was proved at DSDP site 548 (Figure 1), drilled in a water depth of 1256 m on the Goban Spur slope (de Graciansky and Poag, 1985). The base of the Quaternary was placed 101.1 m below sea bed at the top of the Olduvai magnetic event dated at 1.72 Ma (Figure 46). The Pliocene and lower Pleistocene comprises a reddish or greyish clay and nannofossil ooze, whereas the upper Pleistocene to Holocene is a marly, calcareous, foraminiferal, nannofossil ooze. Isolated, ice-rafted pebbles first appear beneath the Pliocene-Pleistocene boundary at 105.6 m below sea bed, implying that Northern hemisphere glaciation commenced in the late Pliocene (Chennaux et al., 1985).

The late Miocene to Recent sequence on the Goban Spur is laterally equivalent to the Little Sole Formation and younger sediments preserved in the interfluves between submarine canyons on the Western Approaches slope. Deposition proceeded through the Pleistocene on these uneroded portions of the slope, though the preserved sequence may not be as complete as on the Goban Spur because of contemporaneous and subsequent mass movement.

THE QUATERNARY SUCCESSION OF THE SOUTHERN PART OF THE CELTIC DEEP BASIN

The northernmost part of the report area lies on the southern margin of the thick and complex Quaternary basin that occupies the Celtic Deep (Figure 9). The southern margin of the sequence is highly irregular, for the southward-thinning Quaternary units are incised by numerous infilled channels formed at, and up to a few kilometres south of, the main Quaternary ice limit (BGS North Celtic Sea Quaternary Geology sheet). Electric logs and bit samples from well 93/2-1 suggest that the section from sea bed to 50 m is coarse-grained, poorly sorted, clayey, glacial outwash containing cobbles. Stiff grey clays, some with chalk clasts, were recovered by gravity coring to the south of the well site (Figure 9). The Quaternary sediments have an irregular base, with a local maximum thickness of about 100 m some 5 km north-east of the well site. The southern termination of the Quaternary succession coincides approximately with the southern margin of the Mesozoic South Celtic Sea Basin. The underlying salt swells in this basin may affect sediments up to the sea bed (Kamerling, 1979), so that this margin of the Quaternary basin may be in part tectonically controlled.

The succession preserved in the Celtic Deep to the north of the report area has a maximum thickness in excess of 200 m, and contains a number of seismic units which include Pleistocene sediments that predate the last major glacial advance. The sea bed at, and south of, well 93/2-1 is flat, and the smooth top of the Pleistocene succession is erosional rather than depositional. This marine erosion surface cuts across the tills and channel infills which were formed during glaciation and the latter stages of deglaciation. Offshore evidence therefore shows that at least one glaciation, probably during the Dimlington Stadial, extended as far south as 50°40′N, and it is likely that the sediments associated with this glacial advance originally extended farther south but were later eroded and dispersed across the shelf. This lends some support to the theories on ice limits across the region proposed by Kellaway et al. (1975) and Wingfield (1990).

HURD DEEP

In size and geometry the Hurd Deep is a unique feature of the area, though similar features are found elswhere on the UK Continental Shelf (Wingfield, 1990). It is an elongate depression about 150 km long and between 1.5 and 5 km wide, orientated east-north-east and lying about 25 km north-west of the Channel Islands (Figure 9). The deep has an undulating long axis reaching a maximum water depth in excess of 170 m, whereas the adjacent sea floor is nearly flat at a depth of between 70 and 90 m. The deep terminates abruptly at its western end, although two similar but smaller features (Fosse d'Ouessant and Fosse de L'Ile Vierge) are found off the French coast to the south-west (Hamilton and Smith, 1972), and a smaller infilled depression lies some 20 km off the Lizard. To the east, the Hurd Deep shallows and opens out into three splays which link with a complex of shallower channels in the central and eastern English Channel (BGS Guernsey Sea Bed Sediment sheet).

The Hurd Deep is incised into Late Cretaceous and Jurassic sediments, and is partially infilled by younger sediments. The trend of the deep is parallel to major faults in the area, but it is not incised along any specific feature in the underlying bedrock. The incision reaches a maximum depth of 240 m, and the thickness of overlying infill exceeds 80 m along extensive lengths of the axis and reaches a maximum of 137 m. It forms a steep-sided valley, often asymmetric in cross-section with at least two, now infilled, side valleys. The infill is stratified on the seismic profiles, and channel erosion and deposition has formed the units into a series of lensoid bodies. Sampling has not penetrated these lenses which are assigned a Quaternary age on the basis of the depositional models outlined below.

Sampling the sea floor around the deep has shown that the sediment cover on the nearly flat adjacent sea bed is often less than half a metre thick. Dredging in the deep has produced bioclastic material and angular to sub-rounded boulders up to 0.4 m across, in part covered by a delicate fauna which demonstrates that they are presently immobile. The Cherbourg Peninsula and Brittany were the main sources for this coarser material, although the larger blocks may have been brought in by ice-rafting (Dangeard, 1929) or river action (Boillot in questions to Hamilton and Smith, 1972).

Hamilton and Smith (1972) proposed that the valley was incised by enhanced tidal scour during a glacial lowstand and partially infilled during subsequent transgression. However, the extreme depth of incision is difficult to explain simply by tidal scour. A catastrophic flood would have the necessary energy, although the source of the water for such an event is in dispute.

A J Smith (1985) invoked a catastrophic theory of breakthrough of the Chalk barrier across the Dover Straits by waters from the North Sea. This flood carved a series of infilled valleys in the Dover Straits, and a linking, anastomosing valley system across the floor of the eastern English Channel. The flood reconcentrated its energy due to topographic focusing north of the Cotentin Peninsula and carved out the Hurd Deep. As the flanks of the deep were near the contemporary sea level, the flood dissipated its energy by cutting the deep and on entering the sea.

Wingfield (1990) argues that enclosed deeps with a similar geometry on the continental shelf surrounding Britain were formed at ice margins by the erosive action of a catastrophic release of water from lakes within ice sheets during deglaciation. According to this theory, the deep was carved by water flowing from west to east, which supports the suggestion of an ice sheet in the western English Channel (Kellaway et al., 1975). However, Wingfield (1990) proposes that the ice was of late Devensian age, while Kellaway et al. (1975) preferred a Wolstonian (Saalian) age. A difficulty with the Wingfield (1990) concept is that most of the anastomosing channels in the eastern Channel coalesce westwards towards the Hurd Deep, implying that the water which cut the deep flowed from east to west. It may not be possible to resolve the problems related to the Hurd Deep without a better knowledge of its preserved Quaternary succession.

MELVILLE FORMATION

Across the broad expanse of the continental shelf, Quaternary deposits are limited in their distribution and difficult to date. Pantin and Evans (1984) defined the Melville Formation in the south-western part of the area as the unit above the upper Little Sole Formation (Figure 46) and beneath the Recent sea-bed sediments and their basal lag (layers A and B respectively). The formation is well developed across the middle and outer shelf, but thins at the landward termination of the tidal sand ridges (Figure 9). It is up to 60 m thick where it is formed into the tidal sand ridges (see Chapter 2), but may thin to nothing between the ridges to leave the Tertiary or early Pleistocene strata covered only by a thin veneer of Layer B and/or A. In the extreme northern part of the area, where a complex suite of Pleistocene units is preserved in the Celtic Deep, the Melville Formation is probably contemporaneous with sediments above the youngest till.

Vibrocores which have penetrated through Layer B into the Melville Formation on the tidal sand ridges have usually encountered clean, sporadically gravelly, sand. The seismic character of the ridges suggests that this material forms the bulk of the unit (Pantin and Evans, 1984). At a number of locations, almost invariably in the troughs between the ridges (Figure 9), vibrocores have recovered material with a glacial aspect overlain by Recent sands, However, an unbedded, stiff, poorly sorted, sandy mud containing lithic clasts (49/-09/44), recovered from the flank of a tidal sand ridge, has the geotechnical properties of lodgement till (Pantin and Evans, 1984). Similar samples have been recovered from topographic lows as far south as 48°19′N at a depth of 210 m (Figure 9). Some samples of till from the deeper-water areas exhibit slump structures. Boulder concentrations, identified on both sea-bed photographs (Hamilton et al., 1980) and sidescan sonar images (BGS Scilly Sea Bed Sediment sheet), are mound-like in form and do not appear to be part of a continuous sheet. It is probable that they, and the minor till accumulations, were dropped from melting icebergs, and are not the basal residue of an ice sheet that once covered the whole western part of the shelf.

At a few locations (Figure 9), vibrocores have recovered sediments with a glaciomarine aspect that are usually yellowish brown, plastic, silty clay with sandy, fining-upward laminae and a small proportion of fine gravel. At site 49/-09/44 this overlies the till-like material. The silty clay contains a rich ostracod/foraminiferal assemblage, and in one sample a molluscan fauna not presently found south of the Arctic Circle (Scourse, in press). Since this site is located on the flank of a tidal sand ridge, the ridges must have existed before glacial conditions retreated from the surrounding region.

The glaciomarine samples were recovered in water depths between 127 m and 180 m and are interpreted as having accumulated beneath an ice shelf which provided a rain of sediment to the sea floor during the latter part of the Dimlington Stadial (Scourse, in press). The distribution of the few samples recovered suggests that the lodgement till samples are grouped in the north, glaciomarine samples on the middle shelf, and slumped tills on the outer shelf (Scourse, in press). They represent a sequence deposited when rising sea level floated off the southern margin of a thin calving ice sheet into a sea with tidal sand ridges at its floor. The maximum grounded ice sheet limit lay near the southern margin of the Celtic Deep at about 50°50′N, though a tongue of ice surged southwards at one time to the Isles of Scilly. If the ridges formed prior to this southward surge, then their abrupt landward termination (Figure 9) might be attributed to erosion by this ice sheet. However, this linear termination of the ridges extends at least as far south as 49°N and there is no other evidence that an ice sheet extended to this latitude.

LAYER B

Belderson and Stride (1966) recognised that in areas near the Cornish coast the 'basal bed of the present sea' (Layer A) did not fully cover the underlying continuous 'rudaceous deposit', here termed Layer B. Layer B is generally a few decimetres thick and consists of poorly sorted, sandy, shelly gravel and coarse sand. The clasts do not normally exceed pebble size, though restricted patches of coarser material ranging up to boulders 0.5 m in diameter have been recognised (Hamilton et al., 1980). The unit forms a carpet of pebbles off the Brittany coast and a distinctive layer of quartzitic sand under Layer A south and west of the Isles of Scilly and the Cornish Peninsula (Bouysse et al., 1979).

Layer B is the lag deposit left as the late Devensian–Flandrian transgression crossed the area and reworked material at the sea bed. The mound-like forms of the glacial debris and boulder concentrations of the Melville Formation are in part contemporaneous with the creation of Layer B, for they were deposited after sea level had started to rise and the water was deep enough to float icebergs. These ice-rafted and glaciomarine deposits accumulated beneath the limit of wave erosion in a water depth greater than 10 to 15 m. To the south, at about 47°N, Pinot (1974) recognised a series of coarse outwash deposits across the shelf that are related to former shorelines and river mouths; these may be equivalent to Layer B and the Melville Formation.

LAYER A

This layer of sediment rarely exceeds one metre in thickness, and has a gradational contact with the underlying Layer B. It represents the sediment transported across the area after decay of the vigorous wave erosion associated with the late Devensian–Flandrian transgression, but does not include the isolated mounds of glacial debris. The upper part of the layer is actively reworked by modern bottom currents, but the base of the unit is presently affected only where the unit is less than about 0.5 m thick. Layer A is a palimpsest sediment (Swift et al., 1971) eroded from a pre-Recent substrate and redeposited under the present hydraulic regime. Little of the terriginous content has been

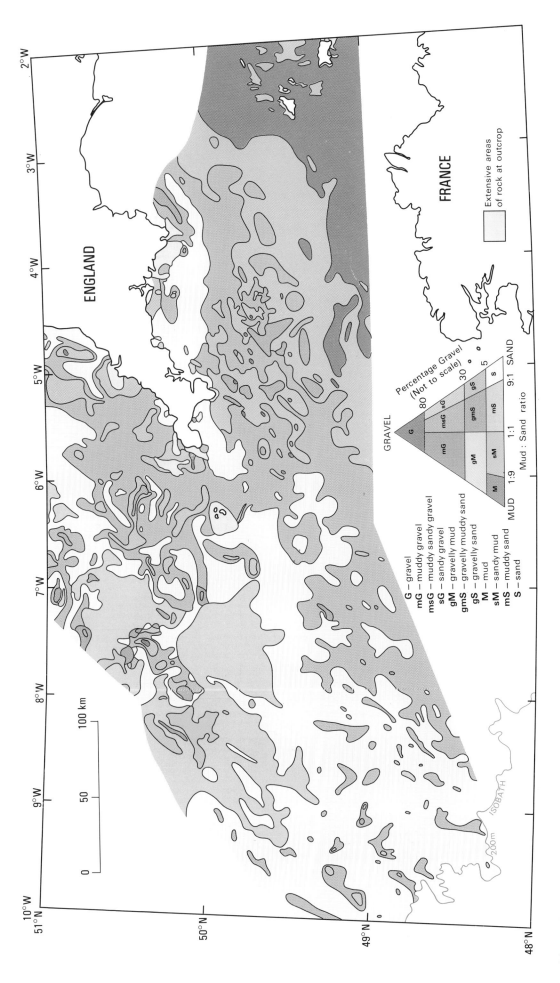

Figure 47 Simplified sea-bed sediment map

derived from coastal erosion, most having been brought into the area by glacial processes.

Some 3000 samples of the unit have been collected, mostly using a Shipek grab which scoops a sample of the sediment some 10 to 15 cm deep from the sea bed and usually destroys any stratification. Mud, sand and gravel proportions of the grab samples have been determined and sediment types defined using a modified Folk (1954) scheme to produce the BGS Sea Bed Sediment maps of the area (Pantin, in press). The simplified version of these maps shown in Figure 47 is similar to the maps produced by Bouysse et al. (1979) and Hamilton et al. (1980).

Gravity coring has proved that the cover of layers A and B is generally less than about half a metre thick across much of the middle and inner shelf. In the central part of the western English Channel, a layer of gravel usually less than 25 cm thick covers the sea bed, and is overlain by sands of Layer A closer to the English coast. Extensive outcrops of bare rock and gravel occur along the coastal zone (Figures 47 and 48), especially off headlands and around shoals. Sidescan sonar profiles from such areas may show extensive rock outcrops where the Shipek grab successfully collected sediment from the sea bed; in these cases the sediment cover is usually less than 0.5 m thick and discontinuous. To the west of the western English Channel as far as the shelf edge, the thin gravelly sands of Layer B are more uniformly overlain by Layer A sand up to about a

metre thick. Currents locally sweep the sand of Layer A into a variety of bedforms to expose the gravelly substrate of Layer B (Hamilton et al., 1980). In the north-western part of the area, Layer A becomes muddier and slightly thicker, except around the Haig Fras shoal.

The grain size and thickness of Layer A is largely a function of the variation in strength of the currents at sea bed across the region. Hamilton et al. (1980) concluded from studies of tidal velocity profiles across the area that all sandy sediments presently at sea bed on the shelf could be moved at some time by bottom currents, and that bottom tidal currents, not waves, are the major control of sediment dispersal. The principal parameter controlling sediment transport and bedform development is the bottom stress (Pingree, 1980), which is a function of water depth, tidal velocity, and the sea-bed roughness. The stresses are greatest in shallow water with strong tidal currents, and weakest in deep water with slack tidal currents. The map of sea-bed sediments correlates well with that of calculated bottom stress (Pingree, 1980); where the stresses are greatest, gravel or bare rock are found at sea bed, whereas muddy sediments and fine sand prevail where they are weakest.

The mean grain size of the sand fraction (Figure 49) shows a similar trend to that displayed by the gross sediment. Coarse sand predominates around the coastal zone, in the central part of the western English Channel and

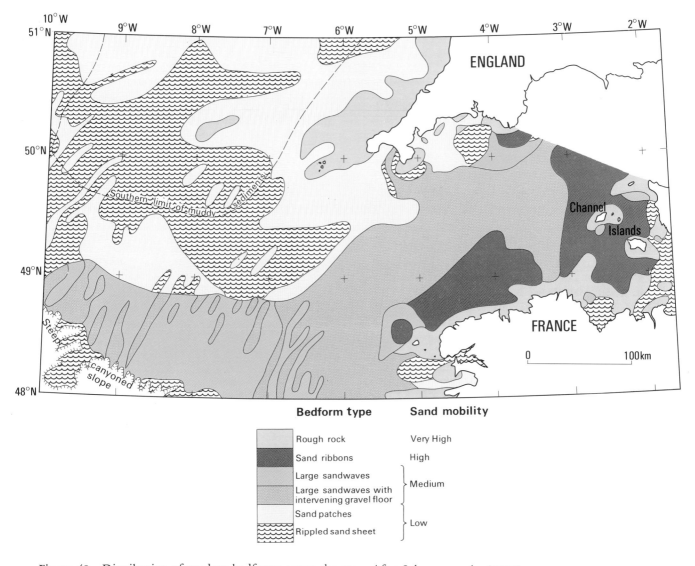

Figure 48 Distribution of modern bedforms across the area. After Johnson et al., (1982)

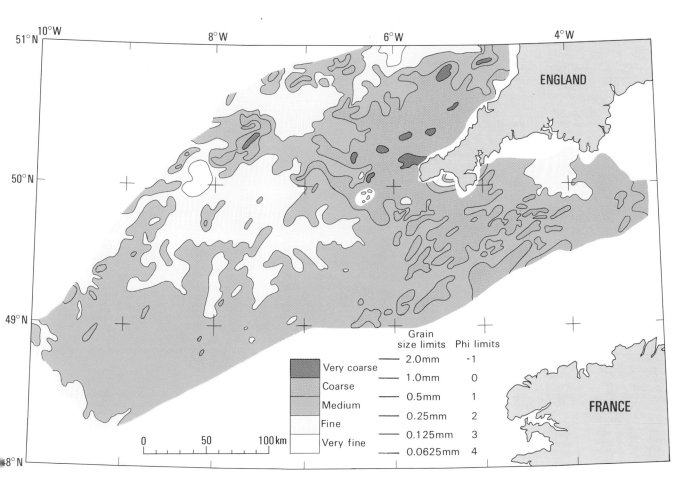

Figure 49 Mean grain size of the sand fraction

around Haig Fras, to pass into medium- to fine-grained sand westwards across to the outer shelf. The finest sand is found in the north-western part of the area where the bottom stress is least, and correlates with the zone of higher mud content (Figure 47).

Sands in the northern part of the area contain irregularly shaped grains of pale to dark green glauconite which infills both the chambers of foraminifera and bored molluscan debris. The glauconite shows no clear relationship with either sediment type or water depth. Some grains have been reworked from Tertiary sediments, but the predominantly pale green form infilling the modern fauna is of Recent origin, for glauconite darkens on burial (George and Murray, 1977).

All the sediments are rich in bioclastic debris, and distinctive faunal assemblages are found associated with the bedform types shown in Figure 48. Polychaetes, molluscs and bryozoans are mostly responsible for breaking down the shell material (Wilson, 1982) which dominates the bioclastic debris across much of the report area. The bioclastic gravel of the area consists of whole or fragmented bivalves, bryozoans, echinoderms, foraminifera, barnacles, gastropods, serpulids and scaphopods (Wilson, 1982). The gravel areas in the western English Channel locally carry a mantle of brittle stars that are associated with rock outcrops (Wilson, 1982). Bryozoans form the main component of the bioclastic debris off the Brittany coast where Lithothamnium is locally dominant. Bivalves predominate in the northern and central parts of the western Channel, and foraminifera are dominant along the outer shelf (Bouysse et al., 1979). The distribution of bryozoan debris indicates that the bioclastic component of the mobile sedi-

ment is being transported westwards and slightly northwards along the shelf. Age determinations on supposed littoral shells collected from the continental shelf west of France gave ages of 9000, 5100 and 3200 years BP at depths of 188 m, 50 m and 32 m respectively (Wilson, 1982).

The bulk of the gravel on the outer shelf is shell debris, although pebbles dominate Layer B and become more abundant where Layer A is thin. The coarsest bioclastic debris is found in ripple troughs, and between spreads of better-sorted sand on the exposed coarser substrate (Hamilton et al., 1980). The carbonate content of the sand fraction (Figure 50) shows limited correlation with its mean grain size, with the highest (>80 per cent) values found north of the Isles of Scilly and the Cornish coast, where the sand fraction is coarsest. However the lowest values (<40 per cent) occur in the medium sands on the outer shelf and south of the Devon coast. Along the outer shelf, the highest concentration of carbonate material occurs on the coarse-grained crests of the tidal sand ridges, due either to locally increased winnowing effects of tidal and possibly wave-induced currents, or to higher biological productivity over the crests (Heathershaw and Codd, 1985).

BEDFORMS

The sediment at sea bed is swept by tide and wave-induced currents into a series of bedforms which range in size from minor ripples to tidal sand ridges. Most of the bedforms in the area are related to the present oceanographic condi-

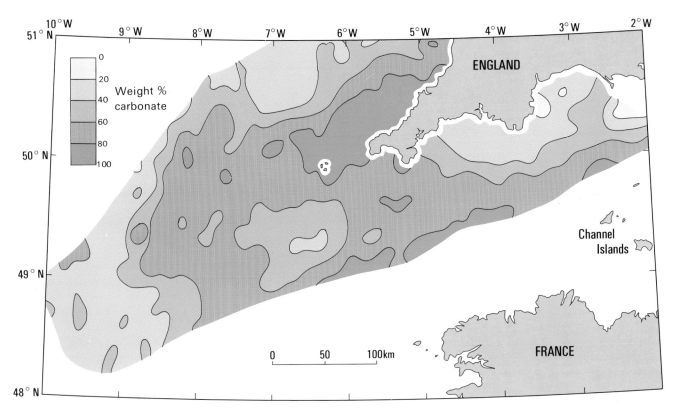

Figure 50   Carbonate content of the sand fraction, statistically simplified

tions, but the tidal sand ridges (see Chapter 2) were formed during a period of lower sea level (Pantin and Evans, 1984).

Oceanography

Aspects of the oceanography discussed here are limited to those which influence the transport of sea-bed sediments and the development of bedforms; primarily the tidal regime (Figures 51 and 52), and secondarily the climate of the area. A wider discussion of the physical oceanography of the area is found in Pingree (1980).

The tidal wave progresses up the English and Bristol channels with co-tidal lines (lines of simultaneous high water) extending almost normal to the coast across the English Channel (Figure 51). The M_2 semidiurnal tide represents the most important tidal wave constituent in the area, and the tidal amplitude at neap tides is about half that of the spring tidal range. In the western portion of the English Channel, the tide is a progressive wave with high water coinciding with the maximum tidal streams.

The speed of the surface tidal stream in the area at spring tide varies from about 0.3 m/s in the Nymphe Bank area of the north Celtic Sea, to about 1.8 m/s in the central English Channel (Figure 52). Extreme values occur off headlands, for example 4.6 m/s off Cap de la Hague in the Alderney race. The tidal stream ellipse is generally rotary clockwise in the Celtic Sea and the westerly entrance to the English Channel. In about 100 m of water, the strength of the tidal stream 1 m from the bottom is about half that of the surface stream.

The annual variation in the temperature structure of the water column for a station in the southern part of Plymouth Bay is shown in Figure 53. A thermocline exists from about June to October, and the timing of its autum-

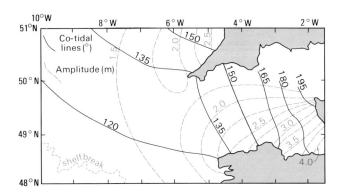

Figure 51   Amplitude (co-range) in metres and co-tidal (lines of simultaneous high water) in degrees of the semi-diurual of M_2 tide.

The co-tidal lines are in degrees of phase lag relative to the passage of the moon over Greenwich. A phase lag increase of 30° implies that high water is one lunar hour later (i.e. 62 minutes). Modified from Pingree (1980).

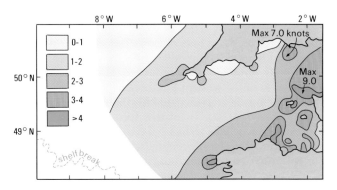

Figure 52   Tidal stream amplitude at spring tides in knots. Simplified from Sager and Sammler (1975).

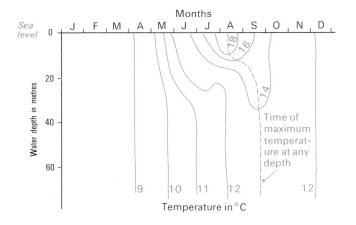

Figure 53 Thermocline development in Plymouth Bay (50°04′N, 3°22′W). From Pingree (1980).

nal destruction extends later into the year westwards in areas of weaker tidal mixing, to persist beyond December across the outer shelf.

The area lies in a region where westerly winds prevail for at least 25 per cent of the time. Gales may occur in any month but are ten times more frequent at midwinter than at midsummer (Cooper, 1967). The significant wave height (exceeded for 50 per cent of the time) at the Seven Stones Light Vessel (see Figure 2 for location) is 2.4 m and is greater to the west, but less to the east (Draper, 1980). The estimated highest waves likely to occur in the area once in 50 years range in height from over 30 m on the outer shelf to over 20 m in the eastern and northern parts of the area. Hamilton et al. (1980) calculate that for fully developed seas in Force 10 winds, the wave orbital velocity down to a depth of 200 m would be able to entrain particles of medium-grained sand up to 0.3 mm in diameter, which is coarser than most sand on the shelf (Figure 49).

Modern bedform distribution

The floor of the central portion of the western English Channel and its extension south-westwards to the shelf edge is covered by sand waves. To the east and along the southern part of the English Channel, the tidal flow is stronger and the sand waves pass into sand ribbons with bare rock exposed near the coast. To the west, and northwards into the Celtic Sea, the tidal stream is weaker and the dominant bedforms are sand patches passing down the sediment transport path into rippled sand sheets. The

suite of bedforms on the sea bed in the area (Figure 48) has been summarised by Johnson et al. (1982). The gross change in bedforms westwards along the English Channel is typical of the variation along a bedload transport path with decreasing velocity of tidal currents (Belderson et al., 1982). However, the absence of sand banks in the western English Channel suggests that the supply of sediment has been limited since the start of the late Devensian–Flandrian transgression.

There are exceptionally large sand waves on the outermost shelf along a band up to 35 km wide parallel to the shelfbreak and down to a water depth of about 200 m. Their crests are up to 5 km long, 1 km apart and 7 m high (Stride, 1963), and their lee slopes have a maximum angle of about 4° (Cartwright and Stride, 1958; Cartwright, 1959). The sand waves are orientated approximately northwest to south-east, parallel to the shelfbreak, and they occur in broad zones within which their asymmetry and size are variable (Hadley, 1964; Heathershaw and Codd, 1985; BGS Little Sole Bank Sea Bed Sediments sheet). On the La Chapelle Bank (Figure 13) south of the report area (47°38′N, 7°15′W), the wavelength of the bedforms decreases from 1000 m to 500 m in 20 km landward away from the shelfbreak, with a concomitant decrease in height from about 9 to 7 m (Heathershaw and Codd, 1985). Current measurements and sea-bed photographs show that the tidal currents alone are able to transport sediment in the area, but an internal wave mechanism is necessary to explain the decrease in wavelength of the bedforms away from the shelfbreak (Heathershaw and Codd, 1985; Heathershaw et al., 1987).

The sea-bed photographs of Hamilton et al. (1980) and Heathershaw and Codd (1985) show that sand ripples are ubiquitous. Symmetrical ripples with wave lengths of up to a metre are developed on the shelf to water depths of at least 160 m, and are often buried by sheets of current-rippled sand. The symmetrical nature of the bedform is attributed to entrainment of the sediment by storm waves (Hamilton et al., 1980; Heathershaw and Codd, 1985).

Where the upper layer of mobile sediment is missing, the thin lag of coarse sand and gravel (Layer B) may be formed into gravel waves with a wave length of about 1.5 m. Well-defined, rounded 'windows' 200 to 300 m wide occur near the crests of the tidal sand ridges in otherwise continuous sand sheets. These windows are probably due to severe turbulance on the crests of the tidal sand ridges and are analogous to kolk-depressions (Pantin and Evans, 1984).

11 Economic geology

The discovery of economic hydrocarbon deposits in the North Sea in the late 1960s encouraged oil companies to explore other sedimentary basins on the continental shelf around the British Isles. Much of the well and deep seismic information used in the preparation of this report has been collected over the past two decades both by companies engaged in hydrocarbon exploration and during the BGS survey programme that was largely funded by the Department of Energy to support this commercial activity. However, this exploration has yet to result in any economic finds of hydrocarbons, and activity has waned since the early eighties. Further economic interest stems from the extensive mineralisation of the country rocks around the Cornubian granites that has supported a mining industry onshore for many centuries.

The data collected during the course of the BGS surveys have provided information that has subsequently been used for a variety of commercial programmes. For example, the knowledge of the sea bed and its substrate has been used during the laying of new fibre-optic telecommunication cables across the area.

HYDROCARBONS

Carboniferous rocks

Strata entrained in the Variscan orogeny across southern England have been regarded as unlikely sources of hydrocarbons because of their deformational history. However, better understanding of the structural style and organic geochemistry of the sediments has recently led to a re-examination of this view (Taylor, 1986).

The Carboniferous (Culm) sandstones and mudstones of north Devon and north Cornwall were folded, metamorphosed and deeply buried during the Late Carboniferous Variscan orogeny. They contain vitrinite organic matter, usually of woody stem or bark that was carried to prodelta and deeper marine sediments from the shallower, coal-rich deltas to the north. Shales from north Devon have a total organic carbon content of between 0.49 and 1.34 per cent, and contain a dominance of gas-prone kerogen (Cornford et al., 1987). Reflectance of the vitrinite in a sediment indicates both the maximum depth of burial of the rock and its quality as a source rock for hydrocarbons. Using this technique, Cornford et al. (1987) concluded that the strata were buried to depths of between 4.5 and 7.0 km prior to thrusting, and that some of the low maturity shales could have generated gas on further post-Variscan burial. However, gas is not considered to have survived in the Carboniferous sediments because maximum burial predated folding, and no coherant cap developed prior to any gas generation.

Jurassic and Cretaceous rocks

When exploration for hydrocarbons started in the area in the early 1970s, the hope was to find extensive thicknesses of Jurassic sediments, which are the main source rocks for hydrocarbon deposits in the northern North Sea and southern England. However, Late Jurassic to Early Creta-ceous erosion has removed much of the Jurassic section across the northern basins of the Western Approaches Trough, and thick Jurassic and Lower Cretaceous sections are preserved only in the southern part of the trough.

The outliers of Liassic (Lower Jurassic) mudstones in the Melville and Plymouth basins are the best source rocks in the northern basins of the Western Approaches Trough. Well 88/2-1, drilled into the eastern part of the Plymouth Bay Basin (Evans et al., 1981), recovered 491 m of Hettangian to Pliensbachian mudstone and shale with limestone intercalations near the base. The total organic carbon values ranged from 3.2 to 11.3 per cent, with the highest values in the Pliensbachian. The samples contain abundant quantities of amorphous (algal) kerogen and sapropelised, vascular plant material of an oil-prone nature. Pyrolysis analyses indicate that the Pliensbachian and Sinemurian strata are good potential sources for oil, whereas the lowermost parts of the Lias exhibit moderate potential.

The maximum depth of the Jurassic in wells from the Melville Basin is 2077 m (73/1-1), though the base of the Jurassic is deeper in the South Celtic Sea Basin. These values relate to the depth below the present surface and do not take into account the extensive Late Jurassic to Early Cretaceous and Eocene to Miocene uplift of the region. In parts of the Western Approaches Trough, Liassic rocks may have been buried at sufficient depth to have generated hydrocarbons before uplift, especially in the Brittany Basin. Overall, the Western Approaches Trough has yielded disappointing exploration results, with no economic finds being reported even within the southern part of the trough where source rocks are most abundant.

Liassic claystones from the Goban Spur area contain mainly inertinitic/woody type organic matter, and have total organic carbon contents of between 1 and 1.5 per cent. The upper part of the sequence is marginally mature for the generation of oil (Cook, 1987).

The only producing offshore field in the region is the Kinsale Head gasfield, lying some 70 km south-south-east of Cork in the North Celtic Sea Basin (Figure 1). The gas consists of thermally generated methane from the Jurassic mixed with biodegraded methane from the fluvial, coal-bearing Wealden facies of Aptian to Albian age which is also the reservoir rock (Colley et al., 1981). The gas is trapped in an anticline, formed during the early Tertiary, that covers an area of 122 km². Similar traps have been sought associated with the salt swells in the Melville Basin, but the Lower Cretaceous succession is not as thick, and the basin did not suffer the same early Tertiary folding and inversion. There may be structures similar to the Kinsale Head anticline in the southern basins of the Western Approaches Trough involving folded, porous, Upper Jurassic sandstones (Hillis, 1988).

MINERALS

The Variscan granites of Devon and Cornwall are surrounded by steeply inclined concentric zones of complex mineralisation that extend about 2 km into their metamorphic aureoles. Minerals such as cassiterite (tin ore), wolframite and tourmaline were deposited nearest the granites, with ores of copper, lead, zinc and iron in the outer zones (Edmonds et al., 1975). Fluorspar and white mica dominate the nonmetallic minerals near to the granite; calcite and dolomite are more common farther away, and quartz is common throughout. Pneumatolitic activity has resulted in the complete kaolinisation of some of the granite. No mineralisation has been recognised from sampling the offshore granites, although Jones et al. (1988) established that the north-eastern granite outcrop at Haig Fras has a softer, more kaolinised lithology than the rest of the body.

The land surface of south-west England has suffered subaerial weathering since Oligocene time, and heavy minerals have been concentrated by fluvial processes into placer deposits close to the mineral source onland, in the rias, and on the continental shelf. Cassiterite has been deposited in the sea-bed sediments both as a result of natural processes and, most significantly, by the erosion and transportation of man-made tailings from land workings. Newsome (1972) estimated that some 11 million kg of placer tin metal are recoverable from the offshore area.

Tooms et al. (1965) ran a survey in Mounts Bay (Figure 10) to establish the offshore margin of the Godolphin granite, and to assess the tin content of the sediments at sea bed. The results indicate that placer deposits are more likely to accumulate on beaches or at the mouths of streams entering the sea, for much of the sea bed is swept clean of sediment. The tin content of the sands offshore varied from 100 to more than 500 ppm, with the highest concentration closest to the coast, and increasing further in the coarser beach sands to attain a value in excess of 5000 ppm on Marazion Beach. This contrasts with a tin content of 10 000 to 20 000 ppm in the sediments of a stream entering the bay at Porthleven.

Off the north coast of the peninsula, Hill and Parker (1970) report the highest tin concentration at St Ives Bay (2850 ppm), with 1325 ppm at Porthtowan and 830 ppm at Perranporth. Tin becomes concentrated in the sands on the shore of Trevaunance Cove near St Agnes after heavy storms, and during the early part of the century a small mill near the beach treated the sand to recover the metal. Yim (1978) reported that offshore between St Agnes Head and Portreath (Figure 9), the thin sheet of superficial, medium- to very fine-grained sand was enriched in tin with concentrations that decreased from a maximum value of about 10 000 ppm near the coast.

The deposits at St Ives Bay have attracted a great deal of interest and, following assays of the deposit (Lee, 1968; Penhale and Hollick, 1968), commercial dredging operations were carried out in 1968 off the Red River Estuary in an area measuring 600 m × 700 m in which the top 0.6 m sand averaged about 0.2 per cent tin metal. The venture failed because of disappointing metallurgical recovery and worse than anticipated problems with poor weather, adverse sea conditions and the large tidal range (Taylor, 1970). Despite this setback, White (1984) reported that following 2 years of pilot testing, construction had begun of an offshore pipeline and onshore concentrator to process tailings with an average of 0.15 per cent tin. Production was targeted at 925 mt/year of tin in concentrates. White (1984) reported that the economic zone lies about 0.5 mile off the coast, ranges from 0.25 to 0.5 miles in width, and occurs as a well-sorted sand layer 0.9 to 1.5 m thick containing reserves of more than 20 million mt.

The infilled submarine coastal valleys such as Restronguet Creek, in the Fal Estuary, carved during the glacial lowstands, have also attracted attention. These valleys could be loci of concentration for detrital cassiterite, but the thickness of overlying sediment often exceeds 15 m (Tooms et al., 1965). Seismic surveys have been used to identify a major buried channel seaward of the Fal and Helford rivers that is infilled with a complex alternation of sand, gravel and clay to a depth of 56 m below OD. Similar narrow channels were identified off the Fowey Estuary and Par Sands. No clearly defined infilled channels linking into the present drainage system were recognised off the north coast of Cornwall, though some patches of sediment aligned parallel to the coast have been identified.

Maërl

Off the Brittany coast, maërl is dredged for use as a fertiliser and soil conditioner, and some 640 000 tonnes were recovered in 1974. Maërl is Lithothamnium, a marine calcareous algae that lives off Brittany to a maximum water depth of about 20 m. The living algae have a reddish purple colour, but the dead algae which form the basis for the extracted material are greyish white after abrasion and disaggregation. Commercially exploitable quantities of maërl have been found in the Fal Estuary on St Mawes Bank, although no large-scale extraction has taken place (Anon, 1977).

References

References to BGS offshore maps are not given, but an index map showing their distribution, and that of 1:50 000 maps on land, is presented inside the back cover.

ADAMS, C J D. 1976. Geochronology of the Channel Islands and adjacent French mainland. *Journal of the Geological Society*, Vol. 132, 233–250.

AINSWORTH, N R, and five others. 1987. Biostratigraphy of the Lower Cretaceous, Jurassic, and uppermost Triassic of the North Celtic Sea and Fastnet Basin. 611–622 in *Petroleum geology of North West Europe*. BROOKS, J and GLENNIE, K W (editors). (London: Graham and Trotman.)

ALLAN, T D. 1961. A magnetic survey in the western English Channel. *Quarterly Journal of the Geological Society of London*, Vol. 117, 157–170.

ANDREIEFF, P, and LEFORT, J-P. 1972. Contribution a l'étude stratigraphique des terrains Secondaires et Tertiaires affleurant en Manche occidentale. *Mémoires du Bureau de Recherches Géologiques et Minières*, Vol. 79, 49–56. [In French.]

— and six others. 1975. The stratigraphy of the post-Palaeozoic sequences in part of the western Channel. *Philosophical Transactions of the Royal Society of London*, Vol. 279A, 79–97.

ANON. 1977. Report of the ICES Working Group on Effects on Fisheries of Marine Sand and Gravel Extraction. *International Council for the Exploration of the Sea, Cooperative Research Report*, No. 64.

AUFFRET, G A, and five others. 1979. Dredged rocks from the Armorican and Celtic margins. 995–1008 in *Initial Reports of the Deep Sea Drilling Project*, Vol. 48. MONTADERT, L, and thirteen others. (Washington: United States Government Printing Office.)

AVEDIK, F. 1975. The seismic structure of the Western Approaches and the South Armorican Continental Shelf and its geological interpretation. 29–43 in *Petroleum and the Continental Shelf of North-West Europe—Volume 1, Geology*. WOODLAND, A W (editor). (Barking: Applied Science Publishers.)

— and five others. 1982. A seismic refraction and reflection study of the continent-ocean transition beneath the north Biscay margin. *Philosophical Transactions of the Royal Society of London*, Vol. 305A, 5–25.

BADHAM, J P N. 1982. Strike-slip orogens—an explanation for the Hercynides. *Journal of the Geological Society*, Vol. 139, 493–504.

BARROW, G. 1906. The geology of the Isles of Scilly. *Memoir of the Geological Survey*, Sheets 357 and 360. (England and Wales.)

BARTON, P, MATTHEWS, D, HALL, J, and WARNER, M. 1984. Moho beneath the North Sea compared on normal incidence and wide-angle seismic records. *Nature, London*, Vol. 308, 55–56.

BEACH, A. 1987. A regional model for linked tectonics in north-west Europe. 43–48 in *Petroleum geology of North West Europe*. BROOKS, J and GLENNIE, K W (editors). (London: Graham and Trotman.)

BELDERSON, R H, JOHNSON, M A, and KENYON, N H. 1982. Bedforms. 27–57 in *Offshore tidal sands—processes and deposits*. STRIDE, A H (editor). (London: Chapman and Hall.)

— and STRIDE, A H. 1966. Tidal current fashioning of a basal bed. *Marine Geology*, Vol. 4, 237–257.

— PINGREE, R D, and GRIFFITHS, D K. 1985. Low sea-level tidal origin of Celtic Sea sand banks—evidence from numerical modelling of M² tidal streams. *Marine Geology*, Vol. 73, 99–108.

BENNET, G, COPESTAKE, P, and HOOKER, N P. 1985. Stratigraphy of the Britoil 72/10-1A well, Western Approaches. *Proceedings of the Geologists' Association*, Vol. 96, 255–261.

BERGGREN, W A, and eleven others. 1980. Towards a Quaternary time scale. *Quaternary Research*, Vol. 13, 277–302.

BIRPS and ECORS. 1986. Deep seismic reflection profiling between England, France and Ireland. *Journal of the Geological Society*, Vol. 143, 45–52.

BOILLOT, G, HORN, R, and LEFORT, J-P. 1972. Évolution structurale de la Manche occidentale au Secondaire et au Tertiaire. *Mémoires du Bureau de Recherches Géologiques et Minières*, Vol. 79, 79–86. [In French.]

BOTT, M H P, DAY, A A, and MASSON-SMITH, D. 1958. The geological interpretation of gravity and magnetic surveys in Devon and Cornwall. *Philosophical Transactions of the Royal Society of London*, Vol. 251A, 161–191.

— HOLDER, A P, LONG, R E, and LUCAS, A L. 1970. Crustal structure beneath the granites of south-west England. 93–102 in Mechanism of igneous intrusion. NEWALL, G, and RAST, N (editors). *Geological Journal Special Issue*, No. 2.

BOUYSSE, P, HORN, R, LAPIERRE, F, and LE LANN, F. 1976. Étude des grands bancs de sable du Sud-est de la mer Celtique. *Marine Geology*, Vol. 20, 251–275. [In French.]

— — and LE LANN, F. 1975. Étude de la structure de la plate-forme continentale méridionale de la mer Celtique entre 7 et 8 degrés ouest. *Revue de l'Institut Français du Pétrole*, Vol. 30, 855–863. [In French.]

— LE LANN, F, and SCOLARI, G. 1979. Les sediments superficiels des Approches Occidentales de la Manche. *Marine Geology*, Vol. 29, 107–135. [In French.]

BRISTOW, C R, EDWARDS, R A, SCRIVENER, R C, and WILLIAMS, B J. 1985. *Geology of Exeter and its environs: geological report for DoE*. (Keyworth, Nottingham: British Geological Survey.)

BROWNE, B C, and COOPER, R I B. 1950. The British submarine gravity surveys of 1938 and 1946. *Philosophical Transactions of the Royal Society of London*, Vol. 242A, 243–310.

BULLARD, E C, and GASKELL, T F. 1941. Submarine seismic investigations. *Proceedings of the Royal Society of London*, Vol. 177A, 476–499.

CAMERON, T D J, STOKER, M S, and LONG, D. 1987. The history of Quaternary sedimentation in the UK sector of the North Sea Basin. *Journal of the Geological Society*, Vol. 144, 43–58.

CARTWRIGHT, D. 1959. On submarine sand-waves and tidal lee-waves. *Proceedings of the Royal Society of London*, Vol. 253A, 218–241.

— and STRIDE, A H. 1958. Large sand waves near the edge of the Continental Shelf. *Nature, London*, Vol. 181, 41.

CASTON, V N D, DEARNLEY, R, HARRISON, R K, RUNDLE, C C, and STYLES, M T. 1981. Olivine-dolerite intrusions in the Fastnet Basin. *Journal of the Geological Society*, Vol. 138, 31–46.

CATT, J A, and STAINES, S J. 1982. Loess in Cornwall. *Proceedings of the Ussher Society*, Vol. 5, 368–375.

CHADWICK, R A. 1985. Permian, Mesozoic and Cenozoic structural evolution of England and Wales in relation to the principles of extension and inversion tectonics. 9–25 in *Atlas of onshore sedimentary basins in England and Wales: post-Carboniferous tectonics and stratigraphy — British Geological Survey.* WHITTAKER, A (editor). (Glasgow and London: Blackie.)

— 1986. Extension tectonics in the Wessex Basin, southern England. *Journal of the Geological Society,* Vol. 143, 465–488.

CHANDLER, M E J. 1964. *The Lower Tertiary floras of southern England; IV. A summary and survey of findings in the light of recent botanical observations.* (London: British Museum, Natural History.)

CHAPMAN, T J. 1988. The Permian to Cretaceous structural evolution of the Western Approaches Basin (Melville sub-basin), UK. 177–200 in Inversion tectonics. COOPER, M A, and WILLIAMS, G D (editors). *Geological Society Special Publication,* No. 44.

CHEADLE, M J, McGEARY, S, WARNER, M R, and MATTHEWS, D H. 1987. Extensional structures on the western UK continental shelf: a review of evidence from deep seismic profiling. 445–465 in Continental extensional tectonics. COWARD, M P, DEWEY, J F, and HANCOCK, P L (editors). *Geological Society Special Publication,* No. 28.

CHENNAUX, G, ESQUEVIN, J, JOURDAN, A, LATOUCHE, C, and MAILLET, N. 1985. X-ray mineralogy and mineral geochemistry of Cenozoic strata (Leg 80) and petrographic study of associated pebbles. 1019–1046 in *Initial reports of the Deep Sea Drilling Project,* Vol. 80. GRACIANSKY, P C de, and fourteen others. (Washington: United States Government Printing Office.)

COLIN, J P, LEHMANN, R A, and MORGAN, B E. 1981. Cretaceous and Late Jurassic biostratigraphy of the North Celtic Sea basin, offshore southern Ireland. 122–155 in *Microfossils from Recent and fossil shelf seas.* NEALE, J W, and BRASIER, M D (editors). (Chichester: Ellis Horwood.)

COLLEY, M G, McWILLIAMS, A S F, and MYERS, R C. 1981. Geology of the Kinsale Head Gas Field, Celtic Sea, Ireland. 504–510 in *Petroleum geology of the Continental Shelf of North-West Europe.* ILLING, L V, and HOBSON, G D (editors). (London: Heyden and Son.)

COLTER, V S, and HAVARD, D J. 1981. The Wytch Farm oil field, Dorset. 494–503 in *Petroleum geology of the Continental Shelf of North-West Europe.* ILLING, L V, and HOBSON, G D (editors). (London: Heyden and Son.)

COOK, D R. 1987. The Goban Spur — exploration in a deep-water frontier basin. 623–632 in *Petroleum geology of North West Europe.* BROOKS, J, and GLENNIE, K W (editors). (London: Graham and Trotman.)

COOPER, L H N. 1967. The physical oceanography of the Celtic Sea. *Oceanography and Marine Biology Annual Review,* Vol. 5, 99–110.

COPE, J C W. 1987. The Pre-Devonian geology of south-west England. *Proceedings of the Ussher Society,* Vol. 6, 468–473.

CORNFORD, C, YARNELL, L, and MURCHISON, D G. 1987. Initial vitrinite reflectance results from the Carboniferous of north Devon and north Cornwall. *Proceedings of the Ussher Society,* Vol. 6, 461–467.

COWARD, M P, and McCLAY, K R. 1983. Thrust tectonics of S Devon. *Journal of the Geological Society,* Vol. 140, 215–228.

— and SMALLWOOD, S. 1984. An interpretation of the Variscan tectonics of SW Britain. 89–102 in Variscan tectonics of the North Atlantic region. HUTTON, D H W, and SANDERSON, D J (editors). *Geological Society Special Publication,* No. 14.

CRAWSHAY, L R. 1908. On rock remains in the bed of the English Channel. An account of the dredgings carried out by ss. 'Oithona' in 1906. *Journal of the Marine Biological Association of the United Kingdom,* Vol. 8, 99–117.

CRONIN, T M. 1983. Rapid sea level and climate change: evidence from continental and island margins. *Quaternary Science Reviews,* Vol. 1, 177–214.

CURRY, D, HAMILTON, D, and SMITH, A J. 1970. Geological and shallow subsurface geophysical investigations in the Western Approaches to the English Channel. *Report of the Institute of Geological Sciences,* No.70/3

— — — 1971. Geological evolution of the western English Channel and its relation to the nearby continental margin. 129–142 in ICSU/SCOR Working Party 31 Symposium, Cambridge 1979: The geology of the East Atlantic Continental Margin. 2. Europe. DELANY, F M (editor). *Report of the Institute of Geological Sciences,* No. 70/14.

— HERSEY, J B, MARTINI, E, and WHITTARD, W F. 1965a. The geology of the Western Approaches of the English Channel — II. Geological interpretation aided by boomer and sparker records. *Philosophical Transactions of the Royal Society of London,* Vol. 248B, 315–351.

— MARTINI, E, SMITH, A J, and WHITTARD, W F. 1962. The geology of the Western Approaches of the English Channel — I. Chalky rocks from the upper reaches of the continental slope. *Philosophical Transactions of the Royal Society of London,* Vol. 245B, 267–290.

— MURRAY, J W, and WHITTARD, W F. 1965b. The geology of the Western Approaches of the English Channel — III. The Globigerina Silts and associated rocks. 239–264 in *Submarine geology and geophysics.* WHITTARD, W F, and BRADSHAW, R (editors). (London: Butterworths.)

— and six others. 1972. Some research projects in submarine geology of the Bristol University Group. *Mémoires du Bureau de Recherches Géologiques et Minières,* Vol. 79, 221–228.

— and six others. 1978. A correlation of Tertiary rocks in the British Isles. *Geological Society Special Report,* No. 12.

DANGEARD, L. 1923. Quelques observations sur la nature géologique et l'origine des 'surfaces pierreuses' de la Manche. *Bulletin de la Société Géologique et Minéalogique de Bretagne,* Vol. 4, 44–47. [In French.]

— 1929. Observations de géologie sous-marine et d'oceanographie relatives a la Manche. *Annales de L'Institut Océanographique,* Vol. 6, 1–295. [In French.]

DARBYSHIRE, D P F, and SHEPHERD, T J. 1985. Chronology of granite magmatism and associated mineralization, S.W. England *Journal of the Geological Society,* Vol. 142, 1159–1177.

DAVIES, G R. 1984. Isotopic evolution of the Lizard Complex. *Journal of the Geological Society,* Vol. 141, 3–14.

DAY, A A. 1959. The continental margin between Brittany and Ireland. *Deep-Sea Research,* Vol. 5, 249–265.

— HILL, M N, LAUGHTON, A S, and SWALLOW, J C. 1956. Seismic prospecting in the Western Approaches of the English Channel. *Quarterly Journal of the Geological Society of London,* Vol. 112, 15–44.

DAY, G A. 1986. The Hercynian evolution of the South West British continental margin. 233–241 in Reflection seismology: the continental crust. *American Geophysical Union, Geodynamics Series,* Vol. 14.

DEARMAN, W R. 1963. Wrench-faulting in Cornwall and South Devon. *Proceedings of the Geologists' Association,* Vol. 74, 265–287.

DEUNFF, J, LEFORT, J-P, and PARIS, F. 1971. Le microplancton ludlovien des formations immergées des Minquiers (Manche) et sa place dans la distribution du paléoplancton silurien. *Bulletin Société Géologique et Minéralogique de Bretagne, Series C,* Vol. 3, 9–28. ÆIn FrenchŒ.

DEWEY, J F. 1982. Plate tectonics and the evolution of the British Isles. *Journal of the Geological Society*, Vol. 139, 371–412.

DIDIER, J, GUENNOC, P, and PAUTOT, G. 1977. Granodiorites, granulites et charnockites de l'eperon de Goban (marge armoricaine) au contact du domaine océanique. *Comptes Rendus des Séances de L'Académie des Sciences, Paris.*

DODSON, M H, and REX, D C. 1971. Potassium-argon ages of slates and phyllites from south-west England. *Journal of the Geological Society*, Vol. 126, 465–499.

DONOVAN, D T. 1972. Geology of the central English Channel. *Mémoires du Bureau de Recherches Géologiques et Minières*, Vol. 79, 215–220.

— and STRIDE, A H. 1975. Three drowned coastlines of probable Late Tertiary age around Devon and Cornwall. *Marine Geology*, Vol. 19, M35–M40.

DOODY, J J, and BROOKS, M. 1986. Seismic refraction investigation of the structural setting of the Lizard and Start complexes, S.W. England. *Journal of the Geological Society*, Vol. 143, 135–140.

DORÉ, F. 1972. La transgression majeure du Paléozoïque infrieur dans le Nord-Est du massif Armoricain. *Bulletin de la Société Géologique de France*, Vol. 714, 79–93. [In French.]

DRAPER, L. 1980. Wave climatology of the U.K. Continental Shelf. 353–368 in *The North-West European shelf seas: the sea bed and the sea in motion—II. Physical and chemical oceanography, and physical resources*. BANNER, F T, COLLINS, M B, and MASSIE, K S (editors). (Amsterdam: Elsevier.)

DURRANCE, E M, and BRISTOW, C M. 1986. Kaolinisation and isostatic readjustment in south-west England. *Proceedings of the Ussher Society*, Vol. 6, 318–322.

— and LAMING, D J C (editors) 1982. *The geology of Devon.* (Exeter: University of Exeter.)

EDMONDS, E A, McKEOWN, M C, and WILLIAMS, M. 1975. *British regional geology: South-West England* (4th edition). (London: HMSO for Institute of Geological Sciences.)

EDWARDS, J W F. 1984. Interpretation of seismic and gravity surveys over the eastern part of the Cornubian platform. 119–124 in *Variscan tectonics of the North Atlantic region*. HUTTON, D H W, and SANDERSON, D H (editors). *Geological Society Special Publication*, No. 14.

EDWARDS, R A. 1976. Tertiary sediments and structure of the Bovey Basins, south Devon. *Proceedings of the Geologists' Association*, Vol. 87, 1–26.

— and FRESHNEY, E C. 1987. Lithostratigraphical classification of the Hampshire Basin Palaeogene deposits (Reading Formation to Head Formation). *Tertiary Research*, Vol. 8, 43–73.

EVANS, C D R, and HUGHES, M J. 1984. The Neogene succession of the South Western Approaches, Great Britain. *Journal of the Geological Society*, Vol. 141, 315–326.

— LOTT, G K, and WARRINGTON, G (compilers). 1981. The *Zephyr* (1977) wells, South-Western Approaches and western English Channel. *Report of the Institute of Geological Sciences*, No. 81/8.

EXLEY, C S. 1966. The granitic rocks of Haig Fras. *Nature, London*, Vol. 210, 365–367.

— 1987. Evidence of crystalline basement west of the Land's End granite, Cornwall: a discussion. *Proceedings of the Geologists' Association*, Vol. 98, 271.

FANNIN, N G T. 1989. Offshore investigations 1966–87. *British Geological Survey Technical Report*, WB/89/02.

FISHER, M J, and JEANS, C V. 1982. Clay mineral stratigraphy in the Permo-Triassic red bed sequences of BNOC 72/10-1A, Western Approaches, and the south Devon coast. *Clay Minerals*, Vol. 17, 79–89.

FLETCHER, B N. 1975. A new Tertiary basin east of Lundy Island. *Journal of the Geological Society*, Vol. 131, 223–225.

FLETT, J S, and HILL, J B. 1946. Geology of the Lizard and Meneage. *Memoir of the Geological Survey of Great Britain*, Sheet 359.

FOLK, R L. 1954. The distinction between grain-size and mineral composition in sedimentary-rock nomenclature. *Journal of Geology*, Vol. 62, 344–359.

FRANCIS, T J G. 1962. Black Mud Canyon. *Deep-Sea Research*, Vol. 9, 457–464.

FRANKE, W, FLOYD, P A, HOLDER, M, and LEVERIDGE, B. 1989. The Rhenohercynian Ocean revisited. *Terra abstracts*, 0507–28, (1), 365.

FRESHNEY, E C, and six others. 1982. A Tertiary basin at Dutson near Launceston, Cornwall, England. *Proceedings of the Geologists' Association*, Vol. 93, 395–402.

GARDINER, P R R, and SHERIDAN, D J R. 1981. Tectonic framework of the Celtic Sea and adjacent areas with special reference to the location of the Variscan Front. *Journal of Structural Geology*, Vol. 3, 317–331.

GEORGE, M, and MURRAY, J W. 1977. Glauconite in Celtic Sea sediments. *Proceedings of the Ussher Society*, Vol. 4, 94–101.

GINZBURG, A, and five others. 1985. The deep seismic structure of the northern continental margin of the Bay of Biscay. *Annales Geophysicae*, Vol. 3, 499–510.

GOODE, A J J, and MERRIMAN, R J. 1987. Evidence of crystalline basement west of the Land's End granite, Cornwall. *Proceedings of the Geologists' Association*, Vol. 98, 39–43.

GRACIANSKY, P C de, and BOURBON, M. 1985. The Goban Spur of the northeast Atlantic Margin during Late Cretaceous times. 863–883 in *Initial reports of the Deep Sea Drilling Project*, Vol. 80. GRACIANSKY, P C de, and fourteen others. (Washington: United States Government Printing Office.)

— and POAG, C W. 1985. Geologic history of Goban Spur, northwest Europe continental margin. 1187–1216 in *Initial reports of the Deep Sea Drilling Project*, Vol. 80. GRACIANSKY, P C de and fourteen others. (Washington: United States Government Printing Office.)

— and seven others. 1987. Organic-rich sediments and palaeoenvironmental reconstructions of the Cretaceous North Atlantic. 317–344 in *Marine petroleum source rocks*. BROOKS, J, and FLEET, A J (editors). *Geological Society Special Publication*, No. 26.

HADLEY, M L. 1964. The Continental Margin southwest of the English Channel. *Deep-Sea Research*, Vol. 11, 767–779.

HALL, S A. 1986. The relationship between regional tectonics, fault development, and halokinesis in the structural development of a half-graben in the Western Approaches. Unpublished MSc thesis, University of Aberdeen.

HALLAM, A. 1981. A revised sea-level curve for the early Jurassic. *Journal of the Geological Society*, Vol. 138, 735–743.

HAMILTON, D. 1979. The geology of the English Channel, South Celtic Sea and Continental Margin, South Western Approaches. 61–87 in *The North-West European shelf seas: the sea bed and the sea in motion–I. Geology and sedimentology*. BANNER, F T, COLLINS, M B, and MASSIE, K S (editors). (Amsterdam: Elsevier.)

— and SMITH, A J. 1972. The origin and sedimentary history of the Hurd Deep, English Channel, with additional notes on other deeps in the western English Channel. *Mémoires du Bureau de Recherches Géologiques et Minières*, Vol. 79, 59–78.

— SOMMERVILLE, J H, and STANFORD, P N. 1980. Bottom currents and shelf, sediments southwest of Britain. *Sedimentary Geology*, Vol. 26, 115–138.

HANCOCK, J M. 1969. Transgression of the Cretaceous sea in south-west-England. *Proceedings of the Ussher Society*, Vol. 2, 61–83.

— and KAUFFMAN, E G. 1979. The great transgressions of the Late Cretaceous. *Journal of the Geological Society*, Vol. 136, 175–186.

HAQ, B U, HARDENBOL, J, and VAIL, P R. 1987. Chronology of fluctuating sea levels since the Triassic. *Science*, Vol. 235, 1156–1167.

HARRISON, R K, SNELLING, N J, MERRIMAN, R J, MORGAN, G E, and GOODE, A J J. 1977. The Wolf Rock, Cornwall: new chemical, isotopic age and palaeomagnetic data. *Geological Magazine*, Vol. 114, 249–264.

HART, M B, and BALL, K C. 1986. Late Cretaceous anoxic events, sea-level changes and the evolution of the planktonic foraminifera. 67–78 *in* North Atlantic palaeoceanography. SUMMERHAYES, C P, and SHACKLETON, N J (editors). *Geological Society Special Publication*, No. 21.

HAWKES, J R. 1981. A tectonic 'watershed' of fundamental consequence in the post-Westphalian evolution of Cornubia. *Proceedings of the Ussher Society*, Vol. 5, 128–131.

HEATHERSHAW, A D, and CODD, J M. 1985. Sandwaves, internal waves and sediment mobility at the shelf-edge in the Celtic Sea. *Oceanologica Acta*, Vol. 8, 391–402.

— — 1986. Depth controlled changes in grain size and calcium carbonate content on a shelf-edge sand bank. *Marine Geology*, Vol.72, 211–224.

— NEW, A L, and EDWARDS, P D. 1987. Internal tides and sediment transport at the shelf break in the Celtic Sea. *Continental Shelf Research*, Vol. 7, 485–517.

HELM, D G. 1984. The tectonic evolution of Jersey, Channel Islands. *Proceedings of the Geologists' Association*, Vol. 95, 1–15.

HENDRIKS, E M L. 1939. The Start–Dodman–Lizard Boundary-Zone in relation to the Alpine structure of Cornwall. *Geological Magazine*, Vol. 76, 385–402.

HERSEY, J B, and WHITTARD, W F. 1966. The geology of the Western Approaches of the English Channel—V. The continental margin and shelf under the the south Celtic Sea. *Geological Survey of Canada*, Paper 66–15, 80–106.

HILL, M N, and KING, W B R. 1953. Seismic prospecting in the English Channel and its geological interpretation. *Quarterly Journal of the Geological Society of London*, Vol. 109, 1–19.

— and LAUGHTON, A S. 1954. Seismic observations in the eastern Atlantic, 1952. *Proceedings of the Royal Society of London*, Vol. 222A, 348–356

— and VINE, F J. 1965. A preliminary magnetic survey of the Western Approaches to the English Channel. *Quarterly Journal of the Geological Society of London*, Vol. 121, 463–475.

HILL, P A, and PARKER, A. 1970. Tin and zirconium in the sediments around the British Isles: a preliminary reconnaissance. *Economic Geology*, Vol. 65, 409–416.

HILLIS, R R. 1988. The geology and tectonic evolution of the Western Approaches Trough. Unpublished PhD thesis, University of Edinburgh.

— and DAY, G A. 1987. Deep events in U.K. South Western Approaches. *Geophysical Journal of the Royal Astronomical Society*, Vol. 89, 243–250

HOLDER, A P, and BOTT, M H P. 1971. Crustal structure in the vicinity of South-west England. *Geophysical Journal of the Royal Astronomical Society*, Vol. 23, 465–489.

HOLDER, M T, and LEVERIDGE, B E. 1986a. A model for the tectonic evolution of south Cornwall. *Journal of the Geological Society*, Vol. 143, 125–134.

— — 1986b. Correlation of Rhenohercynian Variscides. *Journal of the Geological Society*, Vol. 143, 141–147.

HOLLOWAY, S, and CHADWICK, R A. 1986. The Sticklepath–Lustleigh fault zone: Tertiary sinistral reactivation of a Variscan dextral strike-slip fault. *Journal of the Geological Society*, Vol. 143, 447–452.

HORNE, R R, and MACINTYRE, R M. 1975. Apparent age and significance of Tertiary dykes in the Dingle Peninsula, S.W. Ireland. *Scientific Proceedings of the Royal Dublin Society*, Vol. 5A, 293–299.

HOUGHTON, S D, and JENKINS, D G. 1988. Subtropical microfossil indicators from the Late Pliocene Celtic Sea. *Marine Geology*, Vol. 79, 119–126.

HUTHNANCE, J M. 1982. On one mechanism forming linear sand banks. *Estuarine, Coastal and Shelf Science*, Vol. 14, 79–99.

ISAAC, K P, TURNER, P J, and STEWART, I J. 1982. The evolution of the Hercynides of central S.W. England. *Journal of the Geological Society*, Vol. 139, 521–531.

JENKINS, D G. 1977. Lower Miocene planktonic foraminifera from a borehole in the English Channel. *Micropaleontology*, Vol. 23, 297–318.

— 1982. The age and palaeoecology of the St Erth Beds, southern England, based on planktonic foraminifera. *Geological Magazine*, Vol. 119, 201–205.

— and SHACKLETON, N. 1979. Parallel changes in species diversity and palaeotemperature in the Lower Miocene. *Nature, London*, Vol. 278, 50–51.

— WHITTAKER, J E, and CARLTON, R. 1986. On the age and correlation of the St. Erth Beds, S.W. England, based on planktonic foraminifera. *Journal of Micropalaeontology*, Vol. 5, 93–105.

JOHNSON, M A, KENYON, N H, BELDERSON, R H, and STRIDE, A H. 1982. Sand transport. 58–94 in *Offshore tidal sands—processes and deposits*. STRIDE, A H (editor). (London: Chapman and Hall.)

JONES, D G, MILLER, J M, and ROBERTS, P D. 1988. A seabed radiometric survey of Haig Fras, S. Celtic Sea, UK. *Proceedings of the Geologists' Association*, Vol. 99, 193–203.

KAMERLING, P. 1979. The geology and hydrocarbon habitat of the Bristol Channel Basin. *Journal of Petroleum Geology*, Vol. 2, 75–93.

KEEN, D H. 1978. The Pleistocene deposits of the Channel Islands. *Report of the Institute of Geological Sciences*, No. 78/26.

KELLAN, N C. 1975. Submarine geology of Start Bay determined by continuous seismic profiling and core sampling. *Journal of the Geological Society*, Vol. 131, 7–17

KELLAWAY, G A, REDDING, J H, SHEPHARD-THORN, E R, and DESTOMBES, J-P. 1975. The Quaternary history of the English Channel. *Philosophical Transactions of the Royal Society of London*, Vol. 279A, 189–218.

KENNEDY, W J, and JUIGNET, P. 1974. Carbonate banks and slump beds in the Upper Cretaceous (Upper Turonian–Santonian) of Haute Normandie, France. *Sedimentology*, Vol. 21, 1–42.

KENNET, J. 1982. *Marine geology*. (Englewood Cliffs, N J: Prentice-Hall Inc.)

KENYON, N H, BELDERSON, R H, and STRIDE, A H. 1978. Channels, canyons and slump folds on the continental slope between south-west Ireland and Spain. *Oceanologica Acta*, Vol. 1, 369380.

LAKE, S D, and KARNER, G D. 1987. The structure and evolution of the Wessex Basin, southern England: an example of inversion tectonics. *Tectonophysics*, Vol. 137, 347–378.

LAMING, D J C. 1982. The New Red Sandstone. 148–178 in *The geology of Devon*. DURRANCE, E M, and LAMING, D J C (editors). (Exeter: Exeter University.)

LEAKE, R C, and STYLES, M T. 1984. Borehole sections through the Traboe-hornblende schists, a cumulate complex overlying the Lizard peridotite. *Journal of the Geological Society,* Vol. 141, 41–52.

LEE, G S. 1968. Prospecting for tin in the sands of St Ives Bay, Cornwall. *Transactions of the Institution of Mining and Metallurgy,* Vol. A77, 49–64.

LEES, G J. 1974. Petrochemistry of the mica-lamprophyres (minettes) of Jersey (C.I.). *Proceedings of the Ussher Society,* Vol. 3, 149–155.

LEFORT, J P, PEUCAT, J J, DEUNFF, J, and LE HERISSÉ, A. 1985. The Goban Spur Paleozoic Basement. 677–679 in *Initial reports of the Deep Sea Drilling Project,* Vol. 80. GRACIANSKY, P C de, and fourteen others. (Washington: United States Government Printing Office.)

— and SEGOUFIN, J. 1978. Etude compareé des structures profondes et des anomalies magnétiques allongées reconnues en Manche occidentale et en Baie d'Audierne: existence possible d'une suture cryptique au nord-ouest du Massif Armoricain (France). *Tectonophysics,* Vol. 46, 65–76. ÆIn French.Œ

LEVERIDGE, B E, HOLDER, M T, and DAY, G A. 1984. Thrust nappe tectonics in the Devonian of south Cornwall and the western English Channel. 103–12 *in* Variscan tectonics of the North Atlantic Region. HUTTON, D H W and SANDERSON, D J (editors). *Geological Society Special Publication,* No. 14.

LOTT, G K, KNOX, R W O'B, BIGG, P J, DAVEY, R J, and MORTON, A C. 1980. Aptian–Cenomanian stratigraphy in boreholes from offshore south-west England. *Report of the Institute of Geological Sciences,* No. 80/8.

MART, Y, AUFFRET, G A, AUZENDE, J M, and PASTOURET, L. 1979. Geological observations from a submersible dive on the western continental slope of the Armorican Massif. *Marine Geology,* Vol. 31, M61–M68.

MASSON, D G, and MILES, P R. 1986. Development and hydrocarbon potential of Mesozoic sedimentary basins around margins of North Atlantic. *Bulletin of the American Association of Petroleum Geologists,* Vol. 70, 721–729.

— and PARSON, L M. 1983. Eocene deformation on the continental margin S.W. of the British Isles. *Journal of the Geological Society,* Vol. 140, 913–920.

— and ROBERTS, D G. 1981. Late Jurassic–early Cretaceous reef trends on the continental margin S.W. of the British Isles. *Journal of the Geological Society,* Vol. 138, 437–443.

MATTHEWS, D H. 1987. Can we see granites on seismic reflection profiles? *Annales Geophysicae,* Vol. 5B, 353–356.

MAYBURY, C, and WHATLEY, R. 1986. A high diversity ostracod fauna of late Pliocene age from St. Erth, south Cornwall. *Proceedings of the Ussher Society,* Vol. 6, 312–317.

McGEARY, S, CHEADLE, M J, WARNER, M R, and BLUNDELL, D J. 1987. Crustal structure of the continental shelf around Britain derived from BIRPS deep seismic profiling. 33–41 in *Petroleum geology of North West Europe,* BROOKS, J, and GLENNIE, K W (editors). (London: Graham and Trotman.)

— and WARNER, M R. 1985. Seismic profiling the continental lithosphere. *Nature, London,* Vol. 317, 795–797.

McKENZIE, D. 1978. Some remarks on the development of sedimentary basins. *Earth and Planetary Science Letters,* Vol. 40, 25–32.

MEISSNER, R, MATTHEWS, D, and WEVER, Th. 1986. The 'Moho' in and around Great Britain. *Annales Geophysicae,* Vol. 4B, 659–664.

MELVILLE, R V, and FRESHNEY, E C. 1982. *British regional geology: the Hampshire Basin and adjoining areas* (4th edition). (London: HMSO for Institute of Geological Sciences.)

MILLER, J M, ROBERTS, P D, SYMONS, G D, MERRILL, N H and WORMALD, M R. 1977. A towed sea-bed gamma-ray spectrometer for continental shelf surveys. 465–498 in

Nuclear techniques and mineral resources 1977. (Vienna: International Atomic Energy Agency.)

MILLSON, J. 1987. The Jurassic evolution of the Celtic Sea basins. 599–610 in *Petroleum geology of North West Europe.* BROOKS, J, and GLENNIE, K W (editors). (London: Graham and Trotman.)

MITCHELL, G F, and ORME, A R. 1967. The Pleistocene deposits of the Isles of Scilly. *Quarterly Journal of the Geological Society of London,* Vol. 123. 59–92.

— PENNY, L F, SHOTTON, F W and WEST, R G. 1973. A correlation of Quaternary deposits in the British Isles. *Geological Society Special Report,* No. 4.

MONTADERT, L, ROBERTS, D G, DE CHARPAL, O, and GUENNOC, P. 1979. Rifting and subsidence of the northern continental margin of the Bay of Biscay. 1025–1060 in *Initial reports of the Deep Sea Drilling Project,* Vol. 48. MONTADERT, L, and thirteen others. (Washington: United States Government Printing Office.)

MORTON, A C. 1982. Heavy minerals of Hampshire Basin Palaeogene strata. *Geological Magazine,* Vol. 119, 463–476.

MOURANT, A E, 1931. A study of the seismograms of the English Channel earthquakes. *Monthly Notices of the Royal Astronomical Society,* Vol. 2, 374–383.

MUIR WOOD, R. 1989. Fifty million years of 'passive margin' deformation in north west Europe. 7–36 in *Earthquakes at North-Atlantic passive margins: neotectonics and postglacial rebound.* GREGERSEN, S, and HASHAM, P W (editors). (Dordrecht: Kluwer Academic Publishers.)

MÜLLER, C. 1985. Biostratigraphic and paleoenvironmental interpretation of the Goban Spur region based on a study of calcareous nannoplankton. 573–599 in *Initial reports of the Deep Sea Drilling project,* Vol. 80. GRACIANSKY, P C de, and fourteen others. (Washington: United States Government Printing Office.)

MURRAY, J W, and WRIGHT, C A. 1974. Palaeogene foraminiferida and palaeoecology, Hampshire and Paris basins and the English Channel. *Special Papers in Palaeontology, The Palaeontological Association, London,* No. 14.

NEWSOME, C J. 1972. The five 'E's' of oceanology. *Hydrospace,* Vol. 5, 27.

PANTIN, H M. In press. Seabed sediments around the United Kingdom: their bathymetric and physical environment, grain size, mineral composition and associated bedforms. *British Geological Survey Research Report.*

— and EVANS, C D R. 1984. The Quaternary history of the central and southwestern Celtic Sea. *Marine Geology,* Vol. 57, 259–293.

PARKIN, M, and CROSBY, A. 1982. Geological results of boreholes drilled on the southern United Kingdom Continental Shelf by the Institute of Geological Sciences 1969–1982. *Internal Report of the Marine Geology Unit, Institute of Geological Sciences,* No. 82/2.

PASTOURET, L, and seven others. 1981. La marge continentale armoricaine, résultats d'observations en submersible et de dragages dans le canyon Shamrock. *Comptes Rendus des Séances de L'Académie des Sciences,* Vol. 292D, 741–748.[In French.]

— BEUZART, P, and MONTI, S. 1982. Présentation de cartes bathymétriques de la marge continentale armoricaine et celte, golfe de Gascogne. *Bulletin de la Société Géologique de France,* Vol. 24, 407–411. [In French.]

PEDDY, C P, and HOBBS, R W. 1987. Lower crustal reflectivity of the continental margin southwest of Britain. *Annales Geophysicae,* Vol. 5B, 331–338.

PENHALE, J, and HOLLICK, C T. 1968. Beneficiation testing of the St Ives Bay, Cornwall, tin sands. *Transactions of the Institution of Mining the Metallurgy,* Vol. A77, 65–73.

PHILLIPS, F C. 1964. Metamorphic rocks of the sea floor between Start Point and Dodman Point, S.W. England.

Journal of the Marine Biological Association of United Kingdom, Vol. 44, 655–663.

PINET, B, MONTADERT, L, MASCLE, A, CAZES, M, and BOIS, C. 1987. New insights on the structure and the formation of sedimentary basins from deep seismic profiling in Western Europe. 11–31 in *Petroleum geology of North West Europe*. BROOKS, J and GLENNIE, K W (editors). (London: Graham and Trotman.)

PINGREE, R D. 1980. Physical oceanography of the Celtic Sea and English Channel. 415–465 in *The North-West European shelf seas: the sea bed and the sea in motion — II. Physical and chemical oceanography, and physical resources*. BANNER, F T, COLLINS, M B, and MASSIE, K S (editors). (Amsterdam: Elsevier.)

PINOT, J-P. 1974. The continental margin off Brittany — a geomorphological study. Le precontinent Breton entre Penmarc'h, Belle-Ile et l'escarpement continental: etude geomorphologique. Première édition: Etat des traveaux au 1 Novembre 1972, Lannion, Impram. [In French with English abstract.]

POAG, C W, REYNOLDS, L A, MAZZULLO, J M, and KEIGWIN, L D. 1985. Foraminiferal, lithic, and isotopic changes across four major unconformities at Deep Sea Drilling Project Site 548, Goban Spur. 539–555 in *Initial reports of the Deep Sea Drilling Project*, Vol. 80. GRACIANSKY, P C de, and fourteen others. (Washington: United States Government Printing Office.)

POMEROL, C. 1972. Introduction. Colloque sur la géologie de la Manche. *Mémoires du Bureau de Recherches Géologiques et Minières*, No. 79, 11–12. [In French.]

— 1982. *The Cenozoic era: Tertiary and Quaternary*. Translated by Humphries, D W, and Humphries, E E. (Chichester: Ellis Horwood.)

POWELL, A J. 1988. A preliminary investigation into the Neogene dinoflagellate cyst biostratigraphy of the British Southwestern Approaches. *Bulletin des Centres de Recherches Exploration-Production Elf-Aquitaine*, Vol. 12, 277–311.

RATHAN, D G. 1983. The Alderney Sandstone: an alluvial fan. *Proceedings of the Ussher Society*, Vol. 5, 448–453.

RENOUF, J T. 1974. The Proterozoic and Palaeozoic development of the Armorican and Cornubian Provinces. *Proceedings of the Ussher Society*, Vol. 3, 6–43.

RICE-BIRCHALL, B, and FLOYD, P A. 1988. Geochemical and source characteristics of the Tintagel Volcanic Formation. *Proceedings of the Ussher Society*, Vol. 7, 52–55.

ROACH, R, ADAMS, C, BROWN, M, POWER, G, and RYAN, P. 1972. The Precambrian stratigraphy of the Armorican Massif, N.W. France. *24th International Geological Congress*, Section 1, 246–252.

ROBERTS, D G, HUNTER, P M, and LAUGHTON, A S. 1977. *Bathymetry of the Northeast Atlantic. Sheet 2, Continental Margin around the British Isles*. 1:2 400 000 (Taunton: Hydrographer of the Navy for Institute of Oceanographic Sciences.)

— MASSON, D G, MONTADERT, L, and CHARPAL, O de. 1981. Continental Margin from the Porcupine Seabight to the Armorican Marginal Basin. 455–473 in *Petroleum geology of the Continental Shelf of North-West Europe*. ILLING, L V, and HOBSON, G D (editors). (London: Heyden and Son.)

ROBERTS, M C. 1985. The geomorphology and stratigraphy of the Lizard Loess in south Cornwall, England. *Boreas*, Vol. 14, 75–82.

ROBINSON, K W, SHANNON, P M, and YOUNG, D G G. 1981. The Fastnet Basin: an integrated analysis. 444–454 in *Petroleum geology of the Continental Shelf of North-West Europe*. ILLING, L V, and HOBSON, G D (editors). (London: Heyden and Son.)

ROSE, J. 1985. The Dimlington Stadial/Dimlington Chronozone: a proposal for naming the main glacial episode of the Late Devensian in Britain. *Boreas*, Vol. 14, 225–230.

SADLER, P M. 1973. An interpretation of new stratigraphic evidence from south Cornwall. *Proceedings of the Ussher Society*, Vol. 3, 535–550.

SAGER, G, and SAMMLER, R. 1975. *Atlas der Gezeitenströme für die Nordsee, den Kanal und die Irishe See*. (Rostock: Seehydrographischer Dienst der Deutschen Demokratischen Republik.) [In German.]

SCOURSE, J D. 1985. Late Pleistocene stratigraphy of the Isles of Scilly and adjoining regions. Unpublished PhD thesis, University of Cambridge.

— In press. The Isles of Scilly. In *Glacial deposits in Britain and Ireland*. EHLERS, J, GIBBARD, P L, and ROSE, J (editors). (Rotterdam: A A. Balkema.)

SEEMANN, U. 1984. Tertiary intrusives on the Atlantic continental margin off southwest Ireland. *Irish Journal of Earth Sciences*, Vol. 6, 229–236.

SELWOOD, E B, and seven others. 1984. Geology of the country around Newton Abbot. *Memoir of the British Geological Survey*, Sheet 339 (England and Wales).

SHACKLETON, R M, RIES, A C, and COWARD, M P. 1982. An interpretation of the Variscan structures in SW England. *Journal of the Geological Society*, Vol. 139, 533–541.

SMITH, A J. 1985. A catastrophic origin for the palaeovalley system of the eastern English Channel. *Marine Geology*, Vol. 64, 65–75.

— STRIDE, A H, and WHITTARD, W F. 1965. The geology of the Western Approaches of the English Channel — IV. A recently discovered Variscan granite west-north-west of the Scilly Isles. 287–301 in *Submarine geology and geophysics*. WHITTARD, W F, and BRADSHAW, R (editors). (Butterworths: London.)

SMITH, N J P. 1985. Map 2: Contours on the top of the pre-Permian surface of the United Kingdom (South). 1:1 000 000. (Keyworth, Nottingham: British Geological Survey.)

SNELLING, N J. 1985. The chronology of the geological record. SNELLING, N J (editor). *Memoir of the Geological Society*, No. 10.

SNYDER, S W, MULLER, C, and MILLER, K G. 1985. Biostratigraphy and paleoceanography across the Eocene/Oligocene boundary at Deep Sea Drilling Project Site 549. 567–572 in *Initial reports of the Deep Sea Drilling Project*, Vol. 80. GRACIANSKY, P C de, and fourteen others. (Washington: United States Government Printing Office.)

STANLEY, D J, ADDY, S K, and BEHRENS, E W. 1983. The mudline: variability of its position relative to shelfbreak. 279–298 *in* The shelfbreak: critical interface on Continental Margins. STANLEY, D J, and MOORE, G T (editors). *Society of Economic Paleontologists and Mineralogists, Special Publication*, No. 33.

STEPHENS, N. 1970. The West Country and Southern Ireland. 267–314 in *The glaciations of Wales and adjoining regions*. LEWIS, C A (editor). (London: Longmans.)

— 1973. South-west England. 36–45 *in* A correlation of Quaternary deposits in the British Isles. MITCHELL, G F, PENNY, L F, SHOTTON, F W, and WEST, R G (editors). *Geological Society Special Report*, No. 4.

STRIDE, A H. 1963. Current-swept sea floors near the southern half of Great Britain. *Quarterly Journal of the Geological Society of London*, Vol. 119, 175–199

— BELDERSON, R H, KENYON, N H, and JOHNSON, M A. 1982. Offshore tidal deposits: sand sheet and sand bank facies. 95–125 in *Offshore tidal sands — processes and deposits*. STRIDE, A H. (editor). (London: Chapman and Hall.)

STYLES, M T, and RUNDLE, C C. 1984. The Rb-Sr isochron age of the Kennack Gneiss and its bearing on the age of the Lizard Complex, Cornwall. *Journal of the Geological Society*, Vol. 141, 15–19.

Sutton, J, and Watson, J. 1970. The Alderney Sandstone in relation to the ending of Plutonism in the Channel Islands. *Proceedings of the Geologists' Association*, Vol. 81, 577–584.

Swift, D J P, Stanley, D J, and Curray, J R. 1971. Relict sediments on continental shelves, a reconsideration. *Journal of Geology*, Vol. 79, 322–46.

Taylor, J C M. 1986. Gas prospects in the Variscan Thrust Province of Southern England. 37–53 in *Habitat of Palaeozoic gas in NW Europe*. Brooks, J, Goff, J C, and Van Hoorn, B (editors). *Geological Society Special Publication*, No. 23.

Taylor, J T M. 1970. Tin dredging off Cornwall. 591–611 in *Mining and petroleum technology. Proceedings of the Ninth Commonwealth Minerals and Metallurgical Congress, 1969, Volume 1*. Jones, M J (editor). (London: Institute of Mining and Metallurgy.)

Taylor, R T, and Goode, A J J. 1987. Late Pleistocene and Holocene radiocarbon dates from the Penzance district, Cornwall. *Proceedings of the Ussher Society*, Vol. 6, 559.

Thorpe, R S, Cosgrove, M E, and Calsteren, P W C van. 1986. Rare earth element, Sr- and Nd- isotope evidence for petrogenesis of Permian basaltic and K-rich volcanic rocks from south-west England. *Mineralogical Magazine*, Vol. 50, 481–489.

Tombs, J M C. 1977. A study of the space form of the Cornubian granite batholith and its application to detailed gravity surveys in Cornwall. *Mineral Reconnaissance Report, Institute of Geological Sciences*, No. 11.

Tooms, J S, Taylor Smith, D, Nichol, I, Ong, P, and Wheildon, J. 1965. Geochemical and geophysical mineral exploration experiments in Mounts Bay, Cornwall. 363–391 in *Submarine geology and geophysics*. Whittard, W F, and Bradshaw, R (editors). (Butterworths: London.)

Tyson, R V, and Funnell, B M. 1987. European Cretaceous shorelines, stage by stage. *Palaeogeography, Palaeoclimatology, Palaeoecology*. Vol. 59, 69–91.

Van Hoorn, B. 1987. The South Celtic Sea/Bristol Channel Basin: origin, deformation and inversion history. *Tectonophysics*, Vol. 137, 309–334.

Vanney, J-R, and Stanley, D J. 1983. Shelfbreak physiography: an overview. 1–24 *in* The shelfbreak: critical interface on continental margins. Stanley, D J, and Moore, G T (editors). *Society of Economic Paleontologists and Mineralogists, Special Publication* No. 33.

Walsh, P T, Atkinson, K, Boulter, M C, and Shakesby, R A. 1987. The Oligocene and Miocene outliers of west Cornwall and their bearing on the geomorphological evolution of Oldland Britain. *Philosophical Transactions of the Royal Society of London*, Vol. 323A, 211–245.

Warrington, G. 1983. Late Triassic and earliest Jurassic palynomorph assemblages from the Western English Channel and neighbouring areas. *Proceedings of the Ussher Society*. Vol. 5, 473–476.

— and Owens, B. 1977. Micropalaeontological biostratigraphy of offshore samples from south-west Britain. *Report of the Institute of Geological Sciences*, No. 77/7.

— and eight others. 1980. A correlation of Triassic rocks in the British Isles. *Geological Society Special Report*, No. 13.

— and Scrivener, R C. 1988. Late Permian fossils from Devon: regional geological implications. *Proceedings of the Ussher Society*, Vol. 7, 95–96.

— — In press. The Permian of Devon, England. *Review of Palaebotany and Palynology*.

Wernicke, B. 1981. Low-angle normal faults in the Basin and Range Province: nappe tectonics in an extending orogen. *Nature, London*, Vol. 291, 645–648.

White, L. 1984. Cornish tin mining: 1984. *Engineering and Mining Journal*, June 1984, Vol. 185, June, 83–85.

White, N, and McKenzie, D. 1988. Formation of the 'steer's head' geometry of sedimentary basins by differential stretching of the crust and mantle. *Geology*, Vol. 16, 250–253.

Wilkinson, I P, and Halliwell, G P. 1980. Offshore micropalaeontological biostratigraphy of southern and western Britain. *Report of the Institute of Geological Sciences*, No. 79/9.

Wilkinson, G C, Bazley, R A B, and Boulter, M C. 1980. The geology and palynology of the Oligocene Lough Neagh Clays, Northern Ireland. *Journal of the Geological Society*, Vol. 137, 65–75.

Willis-Richards, J. 1986. Three-dimensional modelling from gravity of the Carnmellis Granite Pluton, west Cornwall. (Abstract only). 10th United Kingdom Geophysical Assembly, Glasgow.

Wilson, J B. 1982. Shelly faunas associated with temperate offshore tidal deposits. 126–171 in *Offshore tidal sands—processes and deposits*. Stride, A H (editor). (London: Chapman and Hall.)

Wingfield, R T R. 1990. The origin of major incisions within the Pleistocene deposits of the North Sea. *Marine Geology*, Vol. 91, 31–52.

Wintle, A G. 1981. Thermoluminescence dating of late Devensian loesses in southern England. *Nature, London*, Vol. 289, 479–480.

Wood, A. 1976. Successive regressions and transgressions in the Neogene. *Marine Geology*, Vol. 22, M23–M29.

Worth, R H. 1908. The dredgings of the Marine Biological Association (1895–1906), as a contribution to the knowledge of the geology of the English Channel. *Journal of the Marine Biological Association of the United Kingdom*, Vol. 8, 118–188.

Worzel, J L. 1968. Survey of continental margins. 117–154 in *Geology of shelf seas*. Donovan, D T (editor). (Edinburgh: Oliver and Boyd.)

Yim, W W-S. 1978. Geochemical exploration for offshore tin deposits in Cornwall. 67–77 in *Proceedings of the Eleventh Commonwealth Mining and Metallurgical Congress, Hong Kong*. (London: Institution of Mining and Metallurgy.)

Zagwijn, W H. 1989. The Netherlands during the Tertiary and the Quaternary: a case history of coastal lowland evolution. *Geologie en Mijnbouw*, Vol. 68, 107–120.

Ziegler, P A. 1975. North Sea Basin history in the tectonic framework of North-Western Europe. 131–149 in *Petroleum and the Continental Shelf of North-West Europe*. Woodland, A W (editor). (Barking: Applied Science Publishers.)

— 1982. *Geological atlas of Western and Central Europe*. (Amsterdam: Elsevier for Shell International Petroleum, Maatschappij, BV).

— 1987a. Celtic Sea–Western Approaches area: an overview. *Tectonophysics*, Vol. 137, 285–289.

— 1987b. Evolution of the Western Approaches Trough. *Tectonophysics*, Vol. 137, 341–346.

— 1987c. Late Cretaceous and Cenozoic intra-plate compressional deformations in the Alpine foreland—ageodynamic model. *Tectonophysics*, Vol. 137, 389–420.

Index

BRITISH GEOLOGICAL SURVEY

Keyworth, Nottingham NG12 5GG   (06077) 6111

Murchison House, West Mains Road, Edinburgh EH9 3LA
031-667 1000

London Information Office, Natural History Museum
Earth Galleries, Exhibition Road, London SW7 2DE
071-589 4090

The full range of Survey publications is available by mail
order or over the counter through the Sales Desks at
Keyworth, at Murchison House, Edinburgh, and at the
BGS London Information Office in the Natural History
Museum Earth Galleries. The adjacent museum
bookshop stocks the more popular books for sale over
the counter. Most BGS books and reports are listed in
HMSO's Sectional List 45, and can be bought from
HMSO and through HMSO agents and retailers. Maps
are listed in the BGS Map Catalogue and the Ordnance
Survey's Trade Catalogue, and can be bought from
Ordnance Survey agents as well as from BGS.

*The British Geological Survey carries out the geological
survey of Great Britain and Northern Ireland (the latter
as an agency service for the government of Northern
Ireland), and of the surrounding continental shelf, as
well as its basic research projects. It also undertakes
programmes of British technical aid in geology in
developing countries as arranged by the Overseas
Development Administration.*

*The British Geological Survey is a component body of
the Natural Environment Research Council.*

HMSO publications are available from:

HMSO Publications Centre
(Mail and telephone orders)
PO Box 276, London SW8 5DT
Telephone orders 071-873 9090
General enquiries 071-873 0011
Queueing system in operation for both numbers

HMSO Bookshops
49 High Holborn, London WC1V 6HB   071-873 0011 (Counter service only)
258 Broad Street, Birmingham B1 2HE   021-643 3740
Southey House, 33 Wine Street, Bristol BS1 2BQ   (0272) 264306
9 Princess Street, Manchester M60 8AS   061-834 7201
80 Chichester Street, Belfast BT1 4JY   (0232) 238451
71 Lothian Road, Edinburgh EH3 9AZ   031-228 4181

HMSO's Accredited Agents
(see Yellow Pages)

and through good booksellers